Mathematics Workbook for the GED

JOHANNA HOLM

BARRON'S

All inquiries should be addressed to:
Barron's Educational Series, Inc.
250 Wireless Boulevard
Hauppauge, New York 11788

Library of Congress Catalog Card No. 96-35819

International Standard Book No. 0-8120-9707-6

Library of Congress Cataloging-in-Publication Data

Holm, Johanna.
    Mathematics workbook for the GED / Johanna Holm.
        p.   cm.
    ISBN 0-8120-9707-6
        1. Mathematics—Examinations, questions, etc.
2. General educational development tests—Study guides.
I. Title.
QA43.H595   1997
510'.76—dc20   96-35819
                                          CIP

PRINTED IN THE UNITED STATES OF AMERICA
987654

CONTENTS

Introduction to the GED

The GED is the test of General Educational Development, and is given to adults who did not graduate from high school. When you pass the GED, you will be awarded a certificate that is the equivalent of a high school diploma. Like the diploma, it is regarded as the entry key to the workplace and to higher education.

If you could visit with GED graduates, you would hear stories that bring tears to your eyes, stories that make you want to applaud, and stories full of courage, strength, and goals fulfilled. These successful graduates are like you. They used their life experiences, their determination, and their hard work to move on with their lives by taking this all-important first step. Your passing the GED will open doors for you that have been closed. We wish you the very best on your journey!

History

The GED was established in an effort to help military personnel who were returning from the battlefields of World War II. These were people whose education had been interrupted by war and who were trying now to pick up the pieces of their lives and careers. From those beginnings, the GED has grown so that now one in every seven high school diplomas is awarded through GED. This marvelous program offers a golden opportunity for those tens of thousands for whom the regular high school setting was just not the right plan. The list of GED graduates contains every success story you could think of: small business owners, college graduates, writers, doctors, computer technicians, repair specialists—productive individuals all

across the country. For you, just as it was for them, passing the GED will truly be the first day of the rest of your life.

Intent

It is the intent of this book to be very user friendly. Use it as a road map to get you from where you are today to your successful completion of the GED exam. Even if reading is not your favorite activity, think about this: Every word in this book is there to help you. Every word has a purpose. If you find a word you don't know, look it up.

It is true that everything you know is something you taught yourself. Someone else may have explained it, but you were the one who took it in and made it yours. You taught yourself. This book is carefully designed not only to help you teach yourself enough math to pass the GED, but also to help you gain skills that you can use on the job, in your home, in the marketplace, in your life.

Layout

The layout of this book is modeled after the actual GED. The exam covers the categories of arithmetic skills, measurement, geometry, algebra, number relations, and data analysis. This book has chapters that include each of these topics. Each chapter contains the topics you are likely to see on the GED within that area. They are developed in the most straightforward manner possible. The variety of activities for you to do as you teach yourself is meant to involve your mind so that the learning will be easier. At the end of each of these five chapters, you will find GED-style multiple-choice questions with five answer choices. Taking this test and checking your answers with those provided will let you evaluate your progress. There are explanations given with the answers to enhance your understanding.

In addition to these instructional chapters, there are two chapters for self testing. Chapter 2 is a diagnostic test set up so that you can evaluate your math strengths and weaknesses. A chart at the end of the chapter will allow you to see where you need to concentrate your efforts. The final chapter of the book is a practice exam modeled after the GED. Taking this test will allow you to determine how effective your study has been and to see if additional review of some topics is necessary.

The GED Test

The GED test is made up of five separate tests plus an essay, as shown in the chart below. Some states require that you take all tests on the same day. In other states you may spread the testing over several days.

TEST ORGANIZATION

The mathematics portion of the GED test is called Test 5, and consists of 56 questions to be answered in 90 minutes. These 56 questions are designed so that 20% of them are about geometry ideas, 30% cover topics from algebra, and the remaining 50% are from the area called arithmetic. The arithmetic topics are structured so that 10% concern data analysis: graphs, tables, and statistics . Another 10% are about applications of decimals and fractions, and the remaining 30% deal with measurement of time, money, and space. In short, the math section of the GED will present you with applications that you would find in everyday life.

SAMPLE TEST QUESTIONS

ARITHMETIC: NUMBER RELATIONS

The topic of number relations involves evaluating how one number relates to another.

Test	What Is Included	How Many Items	Time Allowed
Writing Skills (Test 1)	Mechanics Sentence Structure	55	75 minutes
Writing Sample	Essay	1	45 minutes
Social Studies (Test 2)	Geography U.S. History Political Science Economics Behavioral Science	64	85 minutes
Science (Test 3)	Life Sciences Earth Sciences Chemistry Physics	66	95 minutes
Literature and The Arts (Test 4)	Classical Literature Popular Literature Commentary	45	65 minutes
Mathematics (Test 5)	Arithmetic Geometry Algebra	56	90 minutes

Within this area you will find the concepts of ratio, percent, and proportion.

EXAMPLE

Suppose a store is advertising that they are having a special sale, and that every pair of shoes in stock will be 25% off. What would be the selling price of a pair of shoes that cost $60 before the sale?

(1) $45
(2) $30
(3) $25
(4) $20
(5) $15

Answer: (1)

Explanation: To say 25% means to multiply by 0.25.

$$\$60 \times 0.25 = \$15$$

The price would be reduced by $15. The new selling price would be $60 – $15 = $45.

ARITHMETIC: DATA ANALYSIS

Data analysis is the part of the test that requires that you be able to read and interpret graphs, tables, and charts. You will also see questions relating to probability and averages.

EXAMPLE

Suppose your state requires either a minimum grade of 40 on each of the six GED tests or an average of 45 when you consider all the tests. What would your average be if your test results were as follows?

Test	Your Score	Possible Score
Writing Skills	39	80
Writing Sample	38	80
Social Studies	50	80
Science	42	80
Literature	38	80
Mathematics	42	80

(1) 41.5
(2) 42
(3) 42.25
(4) 43
(5) 45

Answer: (1)

Explanation: To find an average, first add all the scores. Then divide by 6 because 6 is the number of scores that you added together. In this case, 249 is the total of all the scores. Then divide 249 by 6. The number 80 is not needed to answer the question.

ARITHMETIC: MEASUREMENT

Measurement questions address your ability to evaluate diagrams and to apply measuring skills to such topics as perimeter, area, volume, time, and space.

EXAMPLE

Suppose you were taking a pre-employment test and one of the questions said to give the number the arrow is pointing to in the diagram below. Which of the following responses is correct?

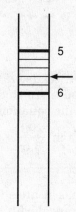

(1) 5.3
(2) 5.4
(3) 5.6
(4) 6.2
(5) 6.4

Answer: (3)

Explanation: First, you should notice that the arrow lies between 5 and 6, so the answer should be 5 decimal point something. Then you should find that each mark represents 0.2. If you had decided each represents 0.1, you would see that there are not enough marks to get from 5 to 6. In starting at the 5 and counting downward, the first mark would be 5.2, then 5.4, and 5.6 at the arrow.

ALGEBRA

The algebra questions on the test will address ideas that include writing and solving equations, using formulas, factoring, and using exponents and ratios.

EXAMPLE

One of the formulas that will be available to you on a separate formula page of the GED is $d = rt$. This is an algebraic way of saying that distance is equal to rate times time. Use this formula to find out how fast you would have to drive in order to cover a distance of 200 miles in exactly 3.5 hours. Which of these choices gives you the correct answer?

(1) $r = \dfrac{200}{3.5}$

(2) $r = 200 \times 3.5$

(3) $r = 3.5 \times 200$

(4) $r = \dfrac{3.5}{200}$

(5) $r = x$

Answer: (1)

Explanation: Because $d = rt$, 200 miles = rate × 3.5 hours. To find the rate, divide both sides of the equation by 3.5 hours.

This results in $\dfrac{200}{3.5}$ = rate.

GEOMETRY

The geometry-based questions on the GED will ask that you deal with lines, angles, and formulas as they relate to circles, squares, rectangles, triangles, and cylinders.

EXAMPLE

Observe the diagram below and calculate the area it shows.

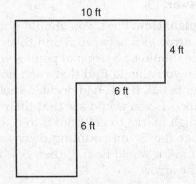

(1) 20 sq. ft.

(2) 40 sq. ft.

(3) 60 sq. ft.

(4) 64 sq. ft.

(5) l00 sq. ft.

Answer: (4)

Explanation: The area of a rectangle can be found by multiplying the length of the rectangle by its width. If you were to split the figure into two separate rectangles as shown below, the area of each rectangle could be calculated. Rectangle #1 has an area of $10 \times 4 = 40$ square feet, while the area of rectangle #2 is $4 \times 6 = 24$ square feet. Adding these two rectangles together gives an area of $24 + 40 = 64$ square feet.

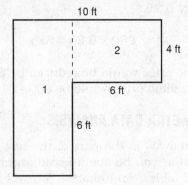

THE ANATOMY OF A QUESTION

Each question on the mathematics test of the GED is built around an everyday application of math, and contains a short descriptive passage, a graph, or a table. Some problems require the use of a formula. A page of formulas will be provided, both on the GED and in this book. In this book's algebra chapter, there is an instructional section on the use of formulas, followed by practice with answers and explanations.

As you evaluate the answer choices provided for a question, remember that some problems include more information than you need, while other problems may not offer enough information, in which case you select the answer that says "Not enough information is given."

The use of calculators is not permitted, so you need to practice the basic operations of addition, subtraction, multiplication, and division. In Chapter 3 you will find explanations and practice.

You will be instructed by the test administrator to use scratch paper, which will be provided, and to record just the answers on the answer sheet. When you have decided on the best choice for the correct answer, fill in the numbered circle that corresponds to that choice. Do not make any marks outside that circle. If you decide to change your answer, be certain to erase completely. Only one answer will be right. Be careful not to wrinkle or fold your answer sheet.

EXAMPLE

If your car gets 20 miles to the gallon of gas, how many gallons will you need to go from your home to Oak Grove and back, if Oak Grove is 150 miles away?

(1) 3
(2) 7.5
(3) 15
(4) 30
(5) Not enough information is given.

Answer: (3)

Fill in your answer on the answer sheet like this: ① ② ● ④ ⑤

Wrong: ① ② ⊗ ④ ⑤

Wrong: ① ② ◑ ④ ⑤

Wrong: ① ② ⊘ ④ ⑤

Explanation: The distance traveled will be 300 miles, since it is a round trip of 150 miles each way. Three hundred miles divided by 20 miles for one gallon gives 15 gallons.

This type of algebraic solution will be covered in depth in the chapter on algebra.

Test-taking Tips

You will not be penalized for wrong answers, so you should answer every question.

In general, if you answer 50 to 60 percent of the test questions correctly, you will pass the test.

The score that is said to be passing is set by each state, province, or territory. The highest score possible on any of the tests within the GED is 80. Each state sets a minimum score requirement and an average score requirement. Suppose your state has a minimum of 40 and an average of 45. This means that you would pass the entire GED if you scored 40 or better on each of the six tests (science, math, literature, etc.). It also means you could pass the entire GED if you fell below the 40 minimum on one or more sections, but you did well enough in other areas to have an average score of at least 45.

Where the GED Is Offered

The location of the GED testing varies from community to community. It will be offered at one or more of these locations: a public library, board of education, community college, adult education center, or a continuing education center. When you contact the appropriate location for your community, you will find out about the testing schedule, identification you will need, fees, and what to bring to the test.

Test-taking Strategies

When you go to take the GED test, it is important that you be comfortable and relaxed. A good night's sleep and a good breakfast will help you to operate efficiently. Comfortable clothing, including a sweater or jacket in case the room is chilly, is a real must. Be certain to provide yourself with tissues, mints, or whatever you can anticipate that you would like to have. Photo identification is usually required.

Try not to be nervous about the test. If you should happen not to do well, you can always take the test again. Some states have a waiting period between tests, which offers you the opportunity for more practice. It should help to know that you have additional chances to do well.

Read all parts of the test carefully, especially the directions. Read each question twice: the first time for a general idea of what the problem is about, and the second time in order to decide how to solve the problem. Read all answer choices, even if you think you know the answer. Once you have read all the choices, you may see one that is better than your original idea.

If you have difficulty with a problem, go on to the next question, making a note to return if time permits. If you cannot determine the correct answer to a problem, try to eliminate any responses that you can. Even if you can eliminate only two responses, you have improved your odds of choosing the right answer.

Wear a watch and pace yourself, knowing that you have 90 minutes for 56 questions. Although you will be busy while taking the test, it is not designed to be an unreasonable amount of work to accomplish in the time allotted. Remember that the GED testing program exists to provide opportunity!

Study Skills

Your successful performance on the GED exam depends on the quality of your preparation. It has been said that you are not really serious about a goal until you have a written plan. Make yourself a calendar of the time between today and the date you plan to be ready to take the exam. Use the table of contents to help you decide how long you can spend with each chapter. Some chapters may come to you more easily than others, so build in a little extra time for a safety net. You can revise your plan later if need be, but now that you have your calendar designed, jump right in—today!

When you learn something new, your brain needs time to "digest" it. Set aside some time each day for your GED work. Even if you can normally spare only 45 minutes a day, make yourself be very faithful to using that 45 minutes well. As you whittle away at your preparation, you will be surprised at the progress you are making. You may also be surprised that 45 minutes will stretch into longer work times as you get hooked on your progress. Usually, getting started is the hardest part.

Your study efficiency will be improved by your study surroundings. You will need a quiet place where you can work without interruption. You will certainly use your time well if you can keep all your study materials together and therefore minimize the time you will need to assemble your books and papers each day.

It will be helpful to make a set of study cards as you work your way through this book. Use index cards, or pieces of paper that you have cut to a convenient size to carry with you. On one side of the card, write the term or idea you want to remember and on the other side draw a picture or use a few words to remind yourself of the meaning. You will never be asked for a definition on the GED, but you will need to be comfortable with ideas. The stack of cards that you make will expand your study time by a surprising number of minutes per day. Just making the cards will improve your understanding of the material. Take the cards with you—in the car, in the kitchen, with you all the time. There are bits of time in every day that you can use for learning.

You can get a feel for the test by doing what the test writers do. They keep their eyes and minds open to ideas while in the supermarket, while on the highway, while in the garage, the kitchen, the yard. Learning to look at life around you in this way will certainly improve your preparation. Remember that the GED has opened doors to millions, and you could be next in line! Now is a marvelous time to begin.

Diagnostic Test

This test is designed to be as similar as possible to the math test of the actual GED. There are 56 questions that reflect the GED standard of 50% arithmetic, 30% algebra, and 20% geometry. You will be allowed 90 minutes for this part of the test, so use that time frame for this diagnostic test.

Answer Sheet for the Diagnostic Test

TEST 5: MATHEMATICS

1. ① ② ③ ④ ⑤	20. ① ② ③ ④ ⑤	39. ① ② ③ ④ ⑤
2. ① ② ③ ④ ⑤	21. ① ② ③ ④ ⑤	40. ① ② ③ ④ ⑤
3. ① ② ③ ④ ⑤	22. ① ② ③ ④ ⑤	41. ① ② ③ ④ ⑤
4. ① ② ③ ④ ⑤	23. ① ② ③ ④ ⑤	42. ① ② ③ ④ ⑤
5. ① ② ③ ④ ⑤	24. ① ② ③ ④ ⑤	43. ① ② ③ ④ ⑤
6. ① ② ③ ④ ⑤	25. ① ② ③ ④ ⑤	44. ① ② ③ ④ ⑤
7. ① ② ③ ④ ⑤	26. ① ② ③ ④ ⑤	45. ① ② ③ ④ ⑤
8. ① ② ③ ④ ⑤	27. ① ② ③ ④ ⑤	46. ① ② ③ ④ ⑤
9. ① ② ③ ④ ⑤	28. ① ② ③ ④ ⑤	47. ① ② ③ ④ ⑤
10. ① ② ③ ④ ⑤	29. ① ② ③ ④ ⑤	48. ① ② ③ ④ ⑤
11. ① ② ③ ④ ⑤	30. ① ② ③ ④ ⑤	49. ① ② ③ ④ ⑤
12. ① ② ③ ④ ⑤	31. ① ② ③ ④ ⑤	50. ① ② ③ ④ ⑤
13. ① ② ③ ④ ⑤	32. ① ② ③ ④ ⑤	51. ① ② ③ ④ ⑤
14. ① ② ③ ④ ⑤	33. ① ② ③ ④ ⑤	52. ① ② ③ ④ ⑤
15. ① ② ③ ④ ⑤	34. ① ② ③ ④ ⑤	53. ① ② ③ ④ ⑤
16. ① ② ③ ④ ⑤	35. ① ② ③ ④ ⑤	54. ① ② ③ ④ ⑤
17. ① ② ③ ④ ⑤	36. ① ② ③ ④ ⑤	55. ① ② ③ ④ ⑤
18. ① ② ③ ④ ⑤	37. ① ② ③ ④ ⑤	56. ① ② ③ ④ ⑤
19. ① ② ③ ④ ⑤	38. ① ② ③ ④ ⑤	

Remove answer sheet by cutting on dotted line

TEST 5: MATHEMATICS

Tests of General Educational Development
Directions*

The Mathematics test consists of multiple-choice questions intended to measure general mathematics skills and problem-solving ability. The questions are based on short readings which often include a graph, chart or figure.

You will have 90 minutes to complete the questions in this test. Work carefully, but do not spend too much time on any one question. Be sure you answer every question. You will not be penalized for incorrect answers.

Formulas you may need are given on page 12. Only some of the questions will require you to use a formula. Not all the formulas given will be needed.

Some questions contain more information than you will need to solve the problem; other questions do not give enough information. If the question does not give enough information to solve the problem, the correct answer choice is "Not enough information is given."

The use of calculators is not allowed.

Do not write in the test booklet. The test administrator will give you blank paper for your calculations. Record your answers on the separate answer sheet provided. Be sure all information is properly recorded on the answer sheet.

To record your answers, fill in the numbered circle on the answer sheet that corresponds to the answer you select for each question in the test booklet.

FOR EXAMPLE:

If a grocery bill totaling $15.75 is paid with a $20.00 bill, how much change should be returned?

(1) $5.26
(2) $4.75
(3) $4.25
(4) $3.75
(5) $3.25

(On Answer Sheet)
① ② ● ④ ⑤

The correct answer is "$4.25"; therefore, answer space 3 would be marked on the answer sheet.

Do not rest the point of your pencil on the answer sheet while you are considering your answer. Make no stray or unnecessary marks. If you change an answer, erase your first mark completely. Mark only <u>one</u> answer space for each question; multiple answers will be scored as incorrect. Do not fold or crease your answer sheet. All test materials must be returned to the test administrator.

DO NOT BEGIN TAKING THE TEST UNTIL TOLD TO DO SO

* Reprinted with permission of the American Council on Education.

TEST 5: MATHEMATICS

FORMULAS*

Description	Formula
AREA (*A*) of a:	
square	$A = s^2$; where s = side
rectangle	$A = \ell w$; where ℓ = length, w = width
parallelogram	$A = bh$; where b = base, h = height
triangle	$A = \frac{1}{2} bh$; where b = base, h = height
circle	$A = \pi r^2$; where r = radius and π is approximately equal to 3.14
PERIMETER (*P*) of a:	
square	$P = 4s$; where s = side
rectangle	$P = 2\ell + 2w$; where ℓ = length, w = width
triangle	$P = a + b + c$; where a, b, and c are the sides
circumference (*C*) of a circle	$C = \pi d$; where d = diameter and π is approximately equal to 3.14
VOLUME (*V*) of a:	
cube	$V = s^3$; where s = side
rectangular container	$V = \ell wh$; where ℓ = length, w = width, h = height
cylinder	$V = \pi r^2 h$; where r = radius, h = height, and π is approximately equal to 3.14
Pythagorean relationship	$c^2 = a^2 + b^2$; where c = hypotenuse, a and b are legs of a right triangle
distance (*d*) between two points in a plane	$d = \sqrt{(x_2 - x_1)^2 + (y_2 - y_1)^2}$; where (x_1, y_1) and (x_2, y_2) are two points in a plane
slope (*m*) of a line	$m = \dfrac{y_2 - y_1}{x_2 - x_1}$; where (x_1, y_1) and (x_2, y_2) are two points on the line
mean	$mean = \dfrac{x_1 + x_2 + \cdots + x_n}{n}$; where the x's are the values for which a mean is desired, and n = number of values for x
median	The *median* is the middle value of an odd number of ordered scores, and halfway between the two middle values of an even number of ordered scores.
simple interest (*i*)	$i = prt$; where p = principal, r = rate, t = time
distance (*d*) as function of rate and time	$d = rt$; where r = rate, t = time
total cost (*c*)	$c = nr$; where n = number of units, r = cost per unit

* Reprinted with permission of the American Council on Education.

TEST 5: MATHEMATICS

<u>Directions:</u> Choose the <u>one best answer</u> to each question.

1. It is often necessary to read a tire pressure gauge. Properly inflated tires not only improve safety, but also save gasoline. How many pounds of pressure are in the tire if the gauge looks like that in the diagram below?

    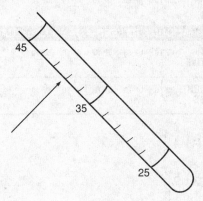

    (1) 35.2
    (2) 36
    (3) 37
    (4) 38
    (5) 39

2. A rug shampoo label states that the proper way to mix the shampoo is to use 1 part of rug shampoo for every seven parts of water. Which of the following choices would be correct?

    (1) 1 soup can shampoo to 7 soup cans water
    (2) $\frac{1}{2}$ cup shampoo to $3\frac{1}{2}$ cups water
    (3) 3 ounces shampoo to 21 ounces water
    (4) All of the above
    (5) None of the above

3. Reducing caloric intake causes weight loss. One pound of fat will be lost for every 3500 calories removed from the normal intake. If a dieter cuts out one canned soda (150 calories) every day, how many pounds will be lost in one year?

    (1) 3500(150)(365)
    (2) $\frac{3500(365)}{150}$
    (3) $\frac{3500(150)}{365}$
    (4) $\frac{150(365)}{3500}$
    (5) $\frac{365}{3500(150)}$

4. The pie graph below shows where the federal government spends money. Which of these statements is an accurate analysis of the graph?

    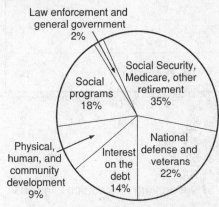

    U.S. Outlay of Federal Money

    (1) Social Security and social programs are equally expensive.
    (2) The United States pays seven times as much on interest as on law enforcement and general government.
    (3) The nation's defense requires more than half of the nation's money.
    (4) For every dollar taken in, the government spends 20 cents on law enforcement.
    (5) Social programs cost the government 18 billion dollars.

GO ON TO THE NEXT PAGE

TEST 5: MATHEMATICS

5. In triangle *ABC* below, $\overleftrightarrow{AD}$ is a straight line. What is $x + y$?

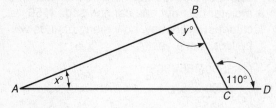

   (1) 60
   (2) 85
   (3) 90
   (4) 110
   (5) Not enough information is given.

6. How many parking spaces could be in a lot with the dimensions shown in the diagram below if the spaces are to be 7 feet wide?

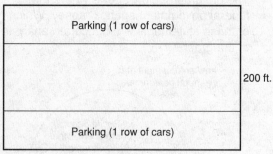

   (1) 25
   (2) 35
   (3) 50
   (4) 100
   (5) Not enough information is given.

7. Jean's car uses approximately 700 gallons of gasoline each year. If premium gasoline costs $1.54 and regular gasoline costs $1.39, how much could Jean save in a year by switching from premium to regular?

   (1) $54.75
   (2) $105.00
   (3) $1050.00
   (4) $1260.00
   (5) Not enough information is given.

8. Suppose that your dog, Daisy, weighed 122 pounds on her last visit to the veterinarian. Since Daisy is not as active as she used to be, you want to watch her diet so she will not get fat. The label below provides feeding information. How many cans of food should Daisy get each day?

FEEDING GUIDELINES						
DOG WEIGHT LBS.	UP TO 5	UP TO 10	UP TO 20	UP TO 50	UP TO 90	OVER 90
AMOUNT TO FEED—374 g/13.2 oz. CANS						
LESS ACTIVE	UP TO ¾	UP TO 1¼	UP TO 2	UP TO 4	UP TO 6	6 PLUS 1 CAN FOR EACH 16 LBS. OVER 90 LBS.
WEIGHT LOSS	UP TO ½	UP TO ¾	UP TO 1½	UP TO 3	UP TO 4½	4½ PLUS 1 CAN FOR EACH 21 LBS. OVER 90 LBS.

   (1) $4\dfrac{1}{2}$
   (2) $5\dfrac{1}{2}$
   (3) 6
   (4) 7
   (5) 8

9. The square root of 50 lies between which pair of numbers?

   (1) 6 and 7
   (2) 7 and 8
   (3) 8 and 9
   (4) 49 and 50
   (5) 50 and 51

GO ON TO THE NEXT PAGE

TEST 5: MATHEMATICS

10. Suppose that a notice appears in the newspaper that states that home owners with trees taller than 50 feet will have to pay an assessment. In order to determine the height of your trees, you recall the idea of similar triangles, and make a diagram as shown below. How tall is the tree?

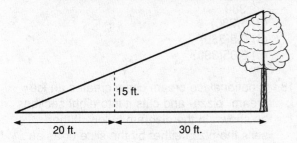

(1) $\dfrac{15(50)}{20}$

(2) $15(50)(20)$

(3) $\dfrac{15(20)}{50}$

(4) $\dfrac{50(20)}{15}$

(5) Not enough information is given.

11. The laws of many states require that hunters wear a minimum of 400 square inches of blaze orange when in the woods in order to improve hunter safety. Study the diagram below. Which choice would provide the hunter with closest to the minimum 400 square inches?

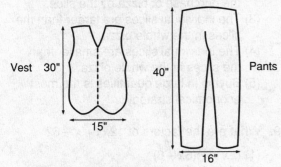

(1) vest, front only
(2) vest, front and back
(3) pants, front only
(4) pants, front and back
(5) vest and pants, front and back

12. Calculate the average number of calories for the first four days of Sandy's diet.

Day one: 1145 calories
Day two: 1395 calories
Day three: 1205 calories
Day four: 1715 calories

(1) 1092
(2) 1115
(3) 1340
(4) 1365
(5) 1390

13. Airplane pilots must consider the fact that they will need more feet of runway for landing when the outside temperature is hot than when it is cold. This is because hot air is less dense than cold air and so does not provide as much resistance to the plane's movement. Which of the following graphs best represents this idea?

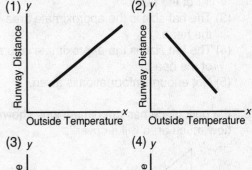

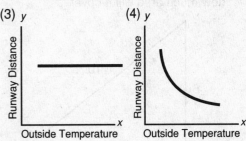

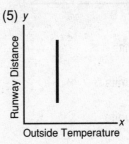

GO ON TO THE NEXT PAGE

TEST 5: MATHEMATICS

14. Find the value of the following expression if $x = 5$ and $y = -3$:

$$4xy - 3x + y$$

   (1) −78
   (2) −66
   (3) −48
   (4) 42
   (5) 72

15. Men's hat sizes are based on the measurement of the circumference of the head. The average man's head is about 23 inches in circumference. If you divide this number by the value for pi of 3.14, you will get about $7\frac{3}{8}$, a common hat size. From the formulas that apply to circles, which of these conclusions can be drawn?

   (1) The hat size is the approximate radius of the head.
   (2) The hat size is the approximate diameter of the head.
   (3) The hat size is the approximate area of the head.
   (4) The hat size is the approximate volume of the head.
   (5) Not enough information is given.

16. If a quilt piece has the dimensions shown, how much area will it cover?

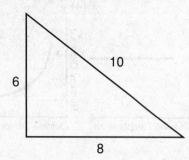

   (1) $\frac{1}{2}$ (8)(6) sq. units

   (2) $\frac{1}{2}$ (10)(8) sq. units

   (3) $\frac{1}{2}$ (10)(6) sq. units

   (4) 6(8) sq. units
   (5) 6 + 8 + 10 sq. units

17. Which of the following gives the correct answer to the question: "What is 5% of 380?"

   (1) $\dfrac{380}{5}$

   (2) $\dfrac{5}{380}$

   (3) 5(380)
   (4) 0.5(380)
   (5) 0.05(380)

18. A national ice cream chain creates an ice cream "pizza" and cuts it into eight sections as shown in the diagram below. It then sells the pizza either by the slice or as an entire pizza. Which of the following statements most accurately analyzes this information?

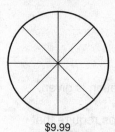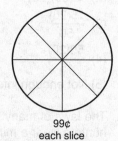

$9.99
one polar pizza
(8 slices)

99¢
each slice

   (1) The highest cost per slice occurs with the purchase of the whole pizza.
   (2) The highest cost per slice occurs with the purchase of pizza by the slice.
   (3) The individual slices are larger than the slices in the whole pizza.
   (4) The individual slices are smaller than the slices in the whole pizza.
   (5) Buying in large quantities is the most economical strategy.

19. What are the factors of $12x^2 + x - 6$?

   (1) $(2x + 1)(6x - 6)$
   (2) $(6x - 3)(2x + 2)$
   (3) $(4x - 6)(3x + 1)$
   (4) $(3x + 2)(4x - 3)$
   (5) $(3x - 2)(4x + 3)$

GO ON TO THE NEXT PAGE

TEST 5: MATHEMATICS

20. For which value of *x* is the inequality
    $3x > -12$ true?

    (1) −9
    (2) −6
    (3) −5
    (4) −4
    (5) 5

21. Which number has the same value as
    10^{-5}?

    (1) −0.000001
    (2) −0.00001
    (3) 0.000001
    (4) 0.00001
    (5) 100,000

22. In order to fence a field, you need a
    measure of its perimeter. To measure the
    perimeter of a field shaped as in the diagram
    below, you make a measuring roller as
    shown. If the wheel goes around 1,000
    times, what is the perimeter of the field?

    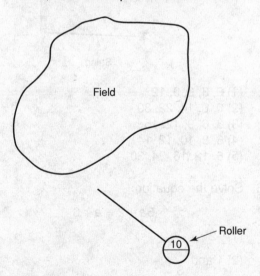

    (1) 1,000
    (2) 1,000(3.14)(5)
    (3) 1,000(3.14)(10)
    (4) 1,000(3.14)(25)
    (5) 1,000(3.14)(100)

23. Current health information suggests that a
    healthy diet is one in which fat provides
    less than 20% of the calories you eat each
    day. Each gram of fat provides 9 calories.
    One of your favorite foods has 15 grams of
    fat. Which choice gives the percent of fat
    that this food represents if your daily intake
    is 2,000 calories?

    (1) 9(0.20)
    (2) 9(15)(2,000)
    (3) $\dfrac{9(15)(100)}{2,000}$
    (4) 9(2,000)(15)
    (5) 9(20%)(15)

24. A 50% antifreeze solution is recommended
    for best protection for the radiator of cars.
    According to the table below, if you were to
    create a 50% antifreeze solution by using 6
    quarts of antifreeze for a 12 quart cooling
    system, to what temperature would your
    car be protected from winter's cold?

Cooling System Capacity (Quarts)	Quarts of Antifreeze Required						
	4	5	6	7	8	9	10
8	−34	−70					
9		−50	−82				
10		−34	−62	−84			
11			−47	−76			
12			−34	−57	−82		
13				−45	−66	−84	
14				−34	−54	−76	
15					−43	−62	−82
16					−34	−52	−70

    (1) −34°
    (2) −50°
    (3) −70°
    (4) −82°
    (5) −84°

GO ON TO THE NEXT PAGE

TEST 5: MATHEMATICS

25. Simplify: $3x - (15 - x) - 3$

    (1) $-14x$
    (2) $2x + 12$
    (3) $4x + 12$
    (4) $2x - 18$
    (5) $4x - 18$

26. According to the graph below, which of the following choices is the correct set of coordinates for point *A*?

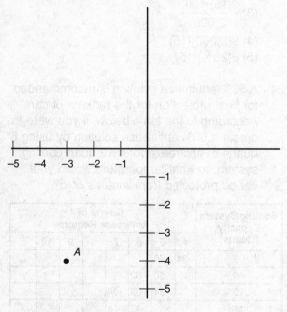

    (1) (3, 4)
    (2) (−3, 4)
    (3) (3, −4)
    (4) (−3, −4)
    (5) Not enough information is given.

27. A target can be made by using a piece of string tied to a pencil. To make a target such as the one in the diagram below, where the bull's eye is 6 inches across and every ring is the same width, how many inches long should the string be for drawing each circle, starting with the bull's eye?

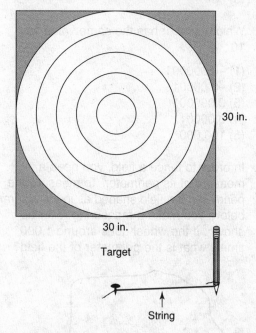

    (1) 0, 3, 6, 9, 12
    (2) 0, 6, 14, 22, 30
    (3) 3, 6, 9, 12, 15
    (4) 6, 8, 10, 12, 14
    (5) 6, 12, 18, 24, 30

28. Solve the equation:

    $$5a - 2 = a + 6$$

    (1) −2
    (2) 1 and $\frac{1}{3}$
    (3) 2
    (4) $\frac{2}{3}$
    (5) $-\frac{2}{3}$

GO ON TO THE NEXT PAGE

TEST 5: MATHEMATICS

29. Inspect the tax rate schedule below and calculate the amount of tax owed on $28,000.

Less than $5,000 ....3% of the taxable income		
At least–	But less than–	
$ 5,000	$12,500	........$ 150.00 plus 4% of excess over $5,000
$12,500	$20,000	........$ 450.00 plus 4.5% of excess over $12,500
$20,000	$30,000	........$ 787.50 plus 6% of excess over $20,000
$30,000		........$1,387.50 plus 6.5% of excess over $30,000

(1) $480.00
(2) $840.00
(3) $1267.50
(4) $1680.00
(5) $12,078.75

30. A fruit-tree sprayer weighs 4 pounds empty and will hold 3 gallons of water. If water weighs 8.4 pounds per gallon, how many pounds will the full sprayer weigh?

(1) 8.4
(2) 12.4
(3) 25.2
(4) 29.2
(5) 37.2

31. Suppose that there was the following activity on one day in your checking account:

(a) deposited $630 check
(b) wrote a check for $125
(c) automatic withdrawal for loan payment of $50
(d) bank-by-mail deposit of $250

Calculate how much this day's activity would change your balance.

(1) +$705
(2) +$805
(3) +$955
(4) +$1055
(5) Not enough information is given.

32. The diagram below is of a fever thermometer. What temperature is indicated by the location of the arrow?

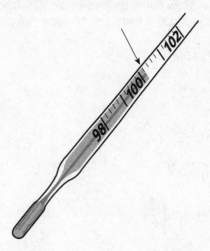

(1) 100.02
(2) 100.2
(3) 100.4
(4) 102
(5) 104

33. The owner's manual for a string trimmer says that a 16:1 ratio of gasoline to 2-cycle oil must be used for its fuel. How many gallons of gasoline would be needed to go with an 8 ounce packet of the oil, if 1 gallon is equal to 128 ounces?

(1) 8
(2) 4
(3) 2
(4) 1
(5) $\frac{1}{2}$

GO ON TO THE NEXT PAGE

TEST 5: MATHEMATICS

34. A leaky faucet can be expensive. Suppose you put a measuring cup under a leak and collect a half cup of water from 8 A.M. to 4 P.M. How many gallons would this amount to in a day if there are 16 cups in a gallon?

    (1) $16(3)\left(\dfrac{1}{2}\right)$

    (2) $\dfrac{3\left(\frac{1}{2}\right)}{16}$

    (3) $\dfrac{16\left(\frac{1}{2}\right)}{3}$

    (4) $\dfrac{16(3)}{\left(\frac{1}{2}\right)}$

    (5) $16(2)\left(\dfrac{1}{2}\right)$

35. The plastic line for string trimmers is available in sizes of 0.080, 0.065, 0.105, and 0.095. These numbers are the diameters of the line in inches. Arrange these string trimmer line sizes from thinnest to thickest.

    (1) 0.105, 0.095, 0.080, 0.065
    (2) 0.065, 0.080, 0.095, 0.105
    (3) 0.080, 0.065, 0.095, 0.105
    (4) 0.105, 0.095, 0.065, 0.080
    (5) 0.105, 0.065, 0.080, 0.095

36. If you were to divide the difference between 28 and 4 by 3 and multiply the result by 2, which of these equations would express these operations?

    (1) $\dfrac{28-4}{3(2)}$

    (2) $2\left(\dfrac{28-4}{3}\right)$

    (3) $\dfrac{28-4(2)}{3}$

    (4) $\left(\dfrac{28+4}{3}\right)2$

    (5) Not enough information is given.

37. In order to keep a chain link gate from sagging, a rod can be installed on the diagonal as shown in the diagram below. Which of the following calculations will give the correct length of the rod?

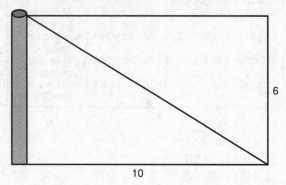

    (1) $\sqrt{6^2+10^2}$
    (2) $36+100$
    (3) $6(10)\left(\dfrac{1}{2}\right)$
    (4) $\dfrac{1}{2}(6+10)$
    (5) Not enough information is given.

38. Express 20,900 in scientific notation.

    (1) 2.09×10^{-4}
    (2) 2.09×10^{-2}
    (3) 0.20900
    (4) 2.09×10^{2}
    (5) 2.09×10^{4}

GO ON TO THE NEXT PAGE

TEST 5: MATHEMATICS

39. You already know that hot air expands. A hot air balloon works in this way. Which of the graphs below shows the relationship that as temperature increases, volume increases?

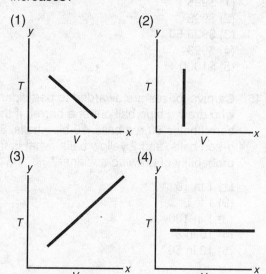

(5) None of the above.

40. A new term that is coming out about diets is called BMI, or body mass index. If the BMI is greater than 30, weight loss is called for. To calculate your BMI multiply your weight by 705. Then divide by your height in inches. Then divide by your height again. Which of these is the correct formula for finding your BMI?

(1) $\text{BMI} = \dfrac{\text{Weight} \times 705}{\text{Height} \times 2}$

(2) $\text{BMI} = \dfrac{\text{Weight} \times 705}{\text{Height}^2}$

(3) $\text{BMI} = \dfrac{\text{Weight} \times 705 \times \text{Height}}{\text{Height}}$

(4) $\text{BMI} = \dfrac{\text{Weight} + 705}{\text{Height} \times 2}$

(5) Not enough information is given.

41. Based on the graph below, which of the following conclusions can you draw?

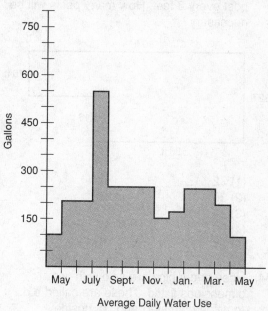

Average Daily Water Use

(1) Water use increases as outside temperature increases.
(2) The daily average use in March was two hundred and fifty gallons.
(3) Heavy August usage was caused by a drought.
(4) May is the month with the heaviest rainfall.
(5) Water use increases steadily after the first of the year.

42. When a credit card company calculates the interest they will charge you for the month, they use a formula that says that principal times rate equals interest, or $P \times R = I$. If your average card balance is $3,000, and you paid $660 interest for the year, what rate is being charged?

(1) 2.2 %
(2) 4.5 %
(3) 6.6 %
(4) 18 %
(5) 22 %

GO ON TO THE NEXT PAGE

TEST 5: MATHEMATICS

43. In buying fence posts for the field shown below, the fencing regulations call for a post every 8 feet. How many posts will be necessary?

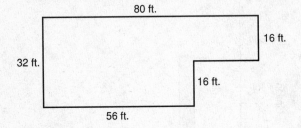

80 ft.

16 ft.

32 ft.

16 ft.

56 ft.

   (1) 32
   (2) 30
   (3) 28
   (4) 26
   (5) 24

44. Hose and tubing are sold with two dimensions listed. These are called o.d. (outside diameter) and i.d. (inside diameter). In the diagram below, which of these dimensions is the thickness of the wall of the hose?

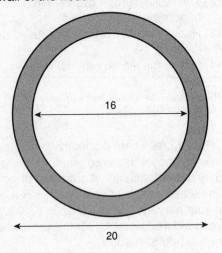

16

20

   (1) 8
   (2) 6
   (3) 4
   (4) 2
   (5) 1

45. The Internal Revenue Service encourages you to round all amounts to the nearest dollar. On your income tax return, how would you record a deduction of $998.48?

   (1) $995
   (2) $998
   (3) $998.50
   (4) $999
   (5) $1000

46. Carnival prizes are awarded to participants who draw a blue ball out of a barrel. If the barrel holds 80 red balls, 10 blue balls, 8 green balls, and 2 yellow balls, what is the probability of drawing a winner?

   (1) 1 in 10
   (2) 1 in 8
   (3) 1 in 100
   (4) 10 in 8
   (5) 10 in 50

47. Simplify: $\dfrac{x^4}{x^{12}}$

   (1) x^{-8}
   (2) x^{-3}
   (3) x^2
   (4) x^3
   (5) x^8

GO ON TO THE NEXT PAGE

TEST 5: MATHEMATICS

48. A hillside will eventually slip if the slope of that hillside is too steep. The slope formula is given in the list of formulas. Use it to calculate the slope shown in the diagram below.

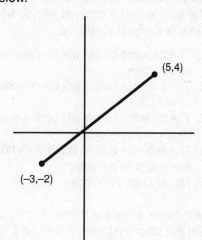

(1) $-\dfrac{3}{4}$

(2) $\dfrac{3}{4}$

(3) $\dfrac{4}{3}$

(4) $-\dfrac{4}{3}$

(5) Not enough information is given.

49. Some health insurance plans are designed so that once the deductible has been met, the patient pays 20% of all doctor's bills. Once the deductible is met, how much would such a patient have to pay on a bill of $120?

(1) $20
(2) $24
(3) $48
(4) $60
(5) $90

50. If you were laying out a baseball diamond, shown in the diagram below, which of these statements would be true?

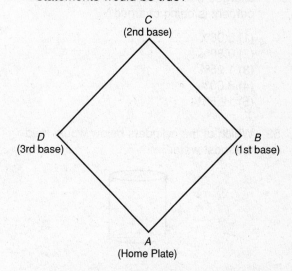

(1) Base path *AB* is parallel to base path *BC*.
(2) Base path *AB* is parallel to base path *CD*.
(3) Base path *AB* is parallel to base path *DA*.
(4) Base path *AB* is parallel to all other base paths.
(5) There are no parallel base paths, since all are at right angles.

51. A stroke patient's blood thinning medicine was changed from 2.5 milligrams to 2.0 milligrams. What percent change is this?

(1) 0.5%
(2) 2.5%
(3) 5.0%
(4) 10.0%
(5) 20.0%

GO ON TO THE NEXT PAGE

TEST 5: MATHEMATICS

52. Suppose that you are shopping while on vacation and buy an item for $125. You are charged $10 in sales tax. What sales tax percent is being charged?

    (1) 0.08%
    (2) 0.80%
    (3) 1.25%
    (4) 8.00%
    (5) 12.50%

53. Which of the cylinders below would hold the most water?

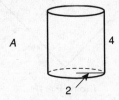

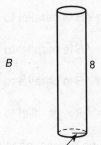

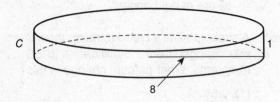

    (1) *A*
    (2) *B*
    (3) *C*
    (4) All cylinders hold the same amount of water.
    (5) Not enough information is given.

54. The instructions on a box of brownie mix call for the brownies to be baked in a square pan that is 8 inches on a side. Suppose that you have only a round pan that is 8 inches across. Compare the areas of a square and a circle to decide which of these is the best response.

    (1) The brownie batter will be deeper in the square pan.
    (2) The brownie batter will be deeper in the round pan.
    (3) The brownie batter will be the same depth in both pans.
    (4) The brownie batter depth depends on the height of the pan.
    (5) Not enough information is given.

55. How many miles are between points *A* and *B* in the diagram below if they lie 2 inches apart on the map and the map scale is such that one-fourth of an inch equals 10 miles?

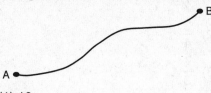

    (1) 10
    (2) 20
    (3) 40
    (4) 80
    (5) 160

56. An equivalency chart in a cookbook shows the following:

    3 teaspoons = 1 tablespoon

    4 tablespoons = $\frac{1}{4}$ cup

    If you needed to measure a half cup and only had a teaspoon to use, how many teaspoonfuls would be required?

    (1) 8
    (2) 12
    (3) 18
    (4) 24
    (5) 32

END OF EXAMINATION

Answer Key

1.	**5**	11.	**1**	21.	**4**	31.	**3**	41.	**2**	51.	**5**
2.	**4**	12.	**4**	22.	**3**	32.	**2**	42.	**5**	52.	**4**
3.	**4**	13.	**1**	23.	**3**	33.	**4**	43.	**3**	53.	**3**
4.	**2**	14.	**1**	24.	**1**	34.	**2**	44.	**4**	54.	**2**
5.	**4**	15.	**2**	25.	**5**	35.	**2**	45.	**2**	55.	**4**
6.	**4**	16.	**1**	26.	**4**	36.	**2**	46.	**1**	56.	**4**
7.	**2**	17.	**5**	27.	**3**	37.	**1**	47.	**1**		
8.	**5**	18.	**1**	28.	**3**	38.	**5**	48.	**2**		
9.	**2**	19.	**5**	29.	**3**	39.	**3**	49.	**2**		
10.	**1**	20.	**5**	30.	**4**	40.	**2**	50.	**2**		

Self-Analysis

WHAT'S YOUR SCORE?

_____right	_____wrong
Excellent	51–56
Good	44–50
Fair	38–43

If your score was low, the explanation of the correct answers that follows will help you. You may obtain additional help by reviewing the self-analysis chart below.

Did you get at least 38 correct answers? If not, you need more practice for the Mathematics Test. You can improve your performance to Good or Excellent by analyzing your errors. To determine the areas in which you need further study, review the chart below. The question numbers from the Diagnostic Test appear in the column to the left. Circle the questions you answered incorrectly. (Unsolved problems are counted as incorrect.) Refer to the Chapter and Chapter Section indicated for each question for additional review.

SELF-ANALYSIS CHART

Question	Chapter	Chapter Section	Question	Chapter	Chapter Section
1.	5	Linear measurement	31.	4	Signed numbers
2.	4	Ratio and proportion	32.	5	Linear measurement
3.	5	Conversion factors	33.	4	Ratio and proportion
4.	7	Graphs		5	Liquid measure
5.	6	Lines and angles	34.	5	Liquid measure
6.	6	Lines and angles			Conversion factor
7.	3	Types of problems	35.	3	Sequencing
8.	7	Tables	36.	4	Translation
9.	4	Exponents	37.	6	Pythagorean
10.	6	Similar triangles			Theorem
	4	Ratio and proportion	38.	4	Scientific notation
11.	6	Area	39.	7	Graphs
12.	7	Average	40.	4	Translation
13.	7	Graphs	41.	7	Graphs
14.	4	Substitution	42.	4	Formulas
15.	6	Shapes			Percent
16.	5	Area	43.	3	Types of problems
17.	4	Percent	44.	6	Shapes
18.	6	Lines and angles	45.	3	Skills
	3	Types of problems	46.	7	Uses of statistics
19.	4	Factoring	47.	4	Exponents
20.	4	Inequalities	48.	4	Formulas
21.	4	Scientific notation	49.	4	Percent
22.	6	Perimeter	50.	6	Lines and angles
		Shapes	51.	4	Percent
23.	4	Percent	52.	4	Percent
24.	7	Tables	53.	6	Volume
25.	4	Order of operations	54.	6	Shapes
26.	4	Coordinates			Volume
27.	6	Shapes	55.	3	Types of problems
28.	4	Solving equations	56.	5	Dry measure
29.	4	Percent			
	7	Tables			
30.	5	Conversion factors			

Answers Explained

1. **5** When checking the scale, the first thing you need to do is to find the value of each of the marks. Here every mark has a value of 2. You can test this by counting from 35 to 45 using the marks. Because each mark is worth 2, start at 35, counting by 2's. This gives 37, 39, 41, 43, 45, which agrees with the numbers on the gauge.

2. **4** Each of the first three choices is a 1-to-7 ratio.

3. **4** $\left(\dfrac{1 \text{ pound}}{3500 \text{ calories}}\right)\left(\dfrac{150 \text{ calories}}{1 \text{ can}}\right)365$ cans

   This strategy is explained in detail in the algebra chapter.

4. **2** When you multiply the 2% spent on law enforcement by 7, you get 14, which is the percent paid in interest.

5. **4** Since $\overleftrightarrow{AD}$ is a straight line, the angle beside the 110° is 180° – 110° = 70°. Then, since the total of the angles in a triangle equals 180°, the sum $x + y$ is 180° – 70° = 110°.

6. **4** In each parking area, you can fit 50 spaces, since 350 ÷ 7 = 50. There are two parking areas, so 50 × 2 = 100.

7. **2** The difference between the two prices is $0.15 per gallon. Multiplying 700 gallons by $0.15 per gallon gives $105.00.

8. **5** Daisy is 32 pounds over the 90 pounds shown on the chart. These 32 pounds allow Daisy to have 2 cans over the 6 shown on the chart for a 90 pound dog. The total cans allowed is 6 + 2 = 8.

9. **2** You can solve this by the process of elimination. The 6 times 7 gives 42, which is too small, but is close. The 8 times 9 is 72, which is too big. Therefore the answer lies between the two numbers.

10. **1** This is a similar triangles problem, so use a proportion. The tree height is to 15 as the big triangle's base of 50 is to the smaller triangle's base of 20.

    This gives the proportion $\dfrac{x}{15} = \dfrac{50}{20}$,

    so $x = \dfrac{15(50)}{20}$.

11. **1** Square inches is a measure of area. The area of a rectangle is the length times the width. The vest's approximate dimensions of 30 by 15 give an area of 450 square inches. Since the vest is the smaller of the two garments, you need to look no further because any other combination will give a number bigger than 450.

12. **4** When you add the four calorie values, you get 5,460. Dividing this by 4 gives an average of 1,365 calories.

13. **1** You are looking for a graph that shows both variables increasing. Choice (1) is the only graph that shows this.

14. **1** Substituting gives the expression 4(5)(–3) – 3(5) – 3, which simplifies to –78.

15. **2** From the formula C = (pi)(diameter), if you substitute the values you know, you get 23 = (3.14)(diameter). To solve for diameter, you divide 23 by 3.14, giving an answer in the range of 7.

16. **1** The quilt piece shown is a triangle. Consulting the formula page shows the area of a triangle to be $\dfrac{1}{2} bh$. Substituting the numbers from the diagram gives an area of $\dfrac{1}{2} (8)(6)$.

17. **5** The word "of" means to multiply. Percents have to be changed into decimals by moving the decimal point two places to the left, so multiply 0.05 and 380.

18. **1** There are two issues here. One is slice size. You can see that there is no indication that the slice size differs when buying a whole pizza or pizza by the slice. The second issue is price. The whole pizza is cut into 8 pieces, so the price of each can be determined by dividing the whole price ($9.99) by 8. Even easier, look at the price of the individual slice at

$.99. If you were to multiply this by 8 to get enough slices to make a whole pizza, you would have nearly $8, which is considerably cheaper than a whole pizza for almost $10.

19. **5** A system that works is to multiply the two expressions in parentheses to see when you get the right answer. This is an algebraic process called FOIL, which is explained in the algebra chapter.

20. **5** You can substitute the various choices and see which works.

21. **4** The negative 5 exponent means to move the decimal point five places in the negative (left) direction.

22. **3** When a wheel rolls, it rolls on its circumference. If the wheel goes around 1,000 times, you have 1,000 circumferences. Since circumference is pi times diameter, $C = (3.14)(10)$. A thousand circumferences equals $3.14(10)(1,000)$.

23. **3** A convenient way to think of percent is that it is part times 100 divided by whole. The whole diet is 2,000 calories. The part from the favorite food is 15 grams times 9 calories per gram.

24. **1** The –34 is the value you get from following the row for a 12 quart cooling system over to the column for 6 quarts of antifreeze.

25. **5** When you remove the parentheses, you get $3x - 15 + x - 3$. The x's sum to $4x$, and the numbers sum to –18.

26. **4** Remember that the x-value is first and the y-value is second. The x-value is –3 and the y-value is –4.

27. **3** The distance from the middle of the target to its outer edge is 15. There are five circles, so each one has a value of 3. Starting at the center, 3 gets you to the first circle, 6 to the second, 9 to the third, and so on.

28. **3**
$$\begin{array}{r} 5a - 2 = a + 6 \\ \underline{-a \qquad -a} \\ 4a - 2 = 0 + 6 \\ \underline{+2 \qquad +2} \\ \dfrac{4a}{4} = \dfrac{8}{4} \\ a = 2 \end{array}$$

29. **3** For $28,000, the taxpayer would owe $787.50 plus 6% of $8,000 (the excess over $20,000).

30. **4** The full sprayer would weigh 4 pounds plus the weight of 3 gallons of water ($3 \times 8.4 = 25.2$). The total is 29.2 pounds.

31. **3** Transactions (a), (b), and (d) are additions. Transaction (c) is a subtraction. $630 + $125 – $50 + $250 = $955

32. **2** One of the best strategies in problems of this sort is to do your best to figure out the answer and then test your answer. For example, if you think that every mark on the thermometer is 0.2 degrees), then see if you can count from one labeled mark to another using this answer.

33. **4** Set up the proportion $\dfrac{1}{16} = \dfrac{8}{x}$, knowing that x will be in ounces because the 8 is in ounces. Solving for x gives $x = 8(16) = 128$ ounces. Since one gallon is 128 ounces, one gallon is the answer.

34. **2** In one day (24 hours) there are 3 of the 8 hour segments. Since the answer must be in gallons, the cups must be changed to gallons by dividing by 16, the number of cups in a gallon.

35. **2** A system that makes dealing with these numbers easier is to move the decimal point (in your mind) three places to the right for every number. Then you can see that the order from smallest to largest is 65, 80, 95, 105.

36. **2** The word "difference" means to subtract, so look for a subtraction of 28 and 4. Then look for a representation of "divide by 3." So far, it looks like it could be any of the first three choices. The final idea, that of multiplying the result by 2, gives you only the possibility of (2). In case (1), the result is divided by 2, and in case (3), only the 4 is multiplied by 2.

37. **1** Check the formula page for the Pythagorean relationship. This problem is an application of that relationship, in which the length of the

rod is the hypotenuse (the side across from the right angle). The length of the rod squared is equal to the sum of the squares of the other two sides of the triangle. In order to find the length of the rod, you must take the square root, which is choice (1).

38. **5** In using scientific notation, the decimal must be placed between the first two digits, so begin with 2.09 (it is not necessary to use the rest of the zeroes). To decide what exponent to use, start with the new location of the decimal and count how many spaces you would have to move to get to the end of the original number. In this case, you would move 4 spaces. Because you are moving to the right (the positive direction), the 4 is positive.

39. **3** Experiment with the graphs by making an imaginary starting point somewhere on the line. Then put another imaginary point on the line at a spot where the temperature would be more than the first point. See what happens to the volume and you will know if you made the right selection.

40. **2** When you read a long problem, try reading just a part of it at a time to see what information you can get out of just that part. The first calculation part of this problem says to multiply weight by 705. This immediately eliminates choice (4). The problem then says to divide by your height, and then divide by height again. This eliminates choice (1) which doubles your height. Choice (3) can be eliminated because it uses height as a multiplier once. Choice (2) is the right selection.

41. **2** As you start working your way through the choices, you need go no further than choice (2) before you encounter the right answer. The only thing that you have to do is to analyze the scale on the left to see that 250 gallons matches March's water use.

42. **5** Substituting $P = 3,000$ and $I = 660$ in the formula $P \times R = I$ gives $3000 \times R = 660$.

Solving for R gives $R = \dfrac{660}{3,000} = 0.22$.

Remember that to find percent, you must multiply the decimal by 100, so the answer is 22%.

43. **3** The most graphic solution to this problem is to use the diagram and put a dot for every post. As you think of how many dots to place, remember that the space between dots represents 8 feet. For example, on a section of the fence that is 32 feet long, there will be dots (posts) at the ends of the section and then dots at 8, 16, and 24 feet.

44. **4** The total diameter of the walls is the difference between 20 and 16, which is 4. Then divide by 2 because there is a wall on the left and a wall on the right.

45. **2** To round to the nearest dollar, look at the cents part. If the cents part is 50 or bigger, add a dollar and round to $999. But the cents portion is less than 50 cents, so you just "throw it away" and make no adjustment, giving you the answer of $998.

46. **1** Probability is the number of good choices out of the number of total choices. In this case the good choices (the blue ones) number 10 and the total choices number 100 (all the balls). When you reduce 10 out of 100, you get 1 out of 10.

47. **1** The algebra rule says that when you divide, you subtract exponents. When you subtract 12 from 4, you get $4 - 12 = -8$.

48. **2** Use of the slope formula (see formula page), gives a slope of $\dfrac{-2-4}{-3-5}$.

So, slope $= \dfrac{-6}{-8} = \dfrac{3}{4}$.

49. **2** Twenty percent of $120 is $0.20 \times 120 = 24$.

50. **2** Parallel means running the same way without ever crossing.

51. **5** Percent can be written: $\dfrac{Part \times 100}{Whole}$.

The part that is changed is $2.5 - 2.0 =$

0.5. The whole is the original, 2.5, so

$$\frac{0.5 \times 100}{2.5} = 20\%.$$

52. **4** Because $125 (tax) = $10, tax = $\frac{10}{25}$ =

0.08. Multiplying by 100% gives a tax rate of 0.08(100%) = 8%.

53. **3** The formula for the volume of a cylinder is given on the formula page. Since pi (3.14) is used in all the calculations, you can leave it out. So, in each case, multiply the height by the radius by the radius. Looking at each cylinder:

A = 4(2)(2) = 16
B = 8(1)(1) = 8
C = 1(8)(8) = 64

Although these numbers are not the real volumes, they have the same relationship as the volumes, so you can see that C is the biggest.

54. **2** If you think of dropping a circular pan down into the square pan, you can see that the square pan includes the corners, while the circular pan does not. This shows that the square holds more than the round pan. This will cause the batter in the round pan to be deeper than in the square pan.

55. **4** Four $\frac{1}{4}$-inch pieces will fit into one inch. Then for 2 inches, you will have 8 of the $\frac{1}{4}$-inch pieces. Since a $\frac{1}{4}$-inch piece represents 10 miles, multiply 10 by 8 to get 80.

56. **4** A half cup is two of the $\frac{1}{4}$ cup sizes, so it contains 8 tablespoons. There are 3 teaspoons in a tablespoon, so multiply 8 by 3 to get 24.

3

Skill Building

Most of the difficulty with math is usually not the "how" part, but the "when" part. For example, you know how to multiply and how to divide, but for some problems, you do not know which should be done. Still, it always helps to practice. This chapter is designed primarily to sharpen your math skills (the "how" part), while the additional chapters are set up to improve your ability to diagnose and solve problems (the "when" part). The chapter is set up so that you have explanations followed by practice. Because practice works only if you have the chance to see if your responses are right, the answers are given at the end of the chapter.

The following topics will be covered in this chapter, followed by practice for the entire chapter.

Calculation Skills
   Arithmetic Operations
   Estimation
   Shortcuts

How to Read a Math Problem
   Symbols
   Vocabulary
   Choosing the Correct Answer
   Set-up Style Answers

Kinds of Problems
   Word Problems
   Whole Numbers
   Fractions
   Decimals
   Sequencing

Calculation Skills

ARITHMETIC OPERATIONS

The first step in developing your math ability is to practice the fundamentals. Since the GED exam does not allow the use of a calculator, you need to become your own calculator. You will be asked to be able to add, subtract, multiply, and divide. Some practice is offered here, and other practice is located in the decimal and fraction parts of this chapter, as well as throughout the book.

PRACTICE

Add the following:

1. 1,009
   +   54

2. 45
   + 8

3. 24,023
   +   250

4.   546
   +2,349

5. 20,075 + 3,672

6. 46 + 3,070

Subtract the following:

7.   7,652
   − 842

8.   9,008
   − 599

9.   140
  − 78

10.   25
   − 16

11.   457 − 274

12.   2,235 − 902

Multiply the following:

13.   703
   × 25

14.   48
   × 25

15.   2,074
   ×   123

16.   400
   × 20

17.   28,003 × 560

18.   354 × 6,721

Divide the following:

19.   45 ÷ 9

20.   50)‾3,050

21. $\dfrac{7,875}{63}$

22. $\dfrac{20,400}{150}$

23.   7,800 ÷ 50

24.   855 ÷ 19

If you find that you need additional practice, set up problems for yourself and check your answers with a calculator. Educational research shows that creating problems helps your understanding.

ANSWERS

1. **1,063**	13. **17,575**
2. **53**	14. **1,200**
3. **24,273**	15. **255,102**
4. **2,895**	16. **8,000**
5. **23,747**	17. **15,681,680**
6. **3,116**	18. **2,379,234**
7. **6,810**	19. **5**
8. **8,409**	20. **61**
9. **62**	21. **125**
10. **9**	22. **136**
11. **183**	23. **156**
12. **1,333**	24. **45**

ESTIMATION

Learn to be an estimator. For example, if you are to multiply 32 by 21, you can tell that the answer is going to be in the vicinity of 600 because 30 times 20 is 600. The value of estimation is that it will improve your accuracy. If you had multiplied 32 times 21 and gotten some number that was very far from 600, you would know to check your calculation.

The easiest way to estimate is to turn the numbers of the problem into easier numbers that are close. Suppose that you are subtracting 762 from 15,842. If you say that the numbers are close to 800 and 16,000, you can subtract and get 15,200. If your actual answer is not close, you know to check your work.

PRACTICE

25. 22 times 735 is equal to *about* what number?

26. 13,864 divided by 42 is equal to *about* what number?

ANSWERS

25. **14,000**
26. **350**

SHORTCUTS

When multiplying or dividing by 10, 100, or another power of 10, you can just move the decimal point and you are finished. For example, 3.19×100 equals 319. The rules to remember follow:

- The number of places the decimal point moves is equal to the number of zeros in the power of 10.
- If multiplying, the decimal point moves to the right.
- If dividing, the decimal point moves to the left.

EXAMPLES

Find 0.35 times 1,000.

The decimal point moves 3 places to the right. The answer is 350.

Find 125 divided by 100.

The decimal point moves 2 places to the left. The answer is 1.25.

Find 20.9 times 100.

The decimal point moves 2 places to the right. The answer is 2,090.

PRACTICE

Perform the indicated operation:

27. $36,726 \times 10,000$

28. $\dfrac{5,647}{100}$

29. $63 \div 1,000$

30. $24 \times 10,000$

ANSWERS

27. **367,260,000** 29. **0.063**
28. **56.47**   30. **240,000**

How to Read a Math Problem

SYMBOLS

Math is a symbolic language. It is more than numbers. Following are symbols that you need to know because they will not be provided on the GED. Any symbols that are unusual, however, will be explained in the test itself.

> means "greater than"
≥ means "greater than or equal to"
< means "less than"
≤ means "less than or equal to"

When looking at the greater than and the less than symbols, remember that the big end of the symbol always points to the side that is larger.

$-\left(\text{as in } \dfrac{12}{4}\right)$ means "divide"

÷ means "divide"

In both cases, divide the first number by the second number.

EXAMPLES

$\dfrac{24}{3}$ means to divide 24 by 3, so $\dfrac{24}{3} = 8$.

$24 \div 6$ means to divide 24 by 6, so $24 \div 6 = 4$

( ) means "do this part first"

EXAMPLES

$(4 + 3) - (2 + 1)$ means to add 4 and 3 to get 7; then add 2 and 1 to get 3; then subtract 3 from 7 to arrive at your answer, 4.

$(8 - 2) \times (10 \div 5)$ means to subtract 2 from 8 to get 6; then divide 10 by 5 to get 2; then multiply 6 by 2 to get your answer, 12.

VOCABULARY

The words in math are very important. Often, every word is important to the meaning, so you do not want to skip even one. Just remember that the words are there to help you with your understanding, and are not intended to make things difficult for you. As you read problems and instructions, try reading the entire problem or a section quickly one time just to see in general what it's about. Then you can go back and read more carefully. Some of the words that you need to watch closely for follow.

"of" can mean to multiply. For example, 20% *of* $500 means to multiply $500 by 20%

"per" means to divide. For example, if you wanted to find the cost per ounce of shampoo, you would divide the price by the ounces of shampoo in the bottle.

CHOOSING THE CORRECT ANSWER

The GED features questions with five possible answers, from which you will choose one. The incorrect answers have been calculated so they will include the most common errors that test takers make. For example, if the correct way to solve a problem were to multiply and then subtract, one of the possible answers would be the result if you subtracted and then multiplied. Remember that the job of a good test maker is to make wrong answers that seem possible, in order to test your skills better.

The best system for choosing the right answer is to do your own calculation of the answer and then to look at the possibilities to see if it is there. If there is a problem for which this does not work for you, try to narrow your choices to just two. At that point, you have at least a 50–50 shot at the right answer. You have no doubt heard that your first impression of the right answer is the best. Once you have narrowed the choices to two, go with your first "gut feeling" about which one of those two to select.

SET-UP STYLE ANSWERS

The GED exam has some questions designed so that your choices of an answer show the steps of problem solving, not the actual answer.

EXAMPLE

Sam worked for 10 hours this week at $5.50 per hour, and also worked 8 hours at $6.00 per hour. Which of the following describes Sam's earnings for the week?

(1) $10 + 5.50 + 8 + 6.00$
(2) $10(5.50 + 6.00) + 8$
(3) $10(5.50) + 8(6.00)$
(4) $10(5.50) \times 8(6.00)$
(5) Not enough information is given.

Answer: (3)

Explanation: As you approach the problem, look first at the 10 hours of work. For this time period the earnings are 10 times $5.50. Then look at the 8 hours of work. Multiplying 8 hours times the $6.00 rate gives these earnings. The final answer is the sum of the two amounts.

Types of Problems

WORD PROBLEMS

The dreaded word problems may seem less threatening if you think of them as life stories. Each word has something to do with the story. Many of the GED math questions tell a story, so you cannot just skip this topic. One of the goals of this book is to make you feel comfortable with stories and word problems.

The following word problems are ones for which you already have the necessary skills. Jump right in and see what you can do with them.

PRACTICE

31. In the world of making money by investing, there is what is called the "rule of 72." This rule says that your money will double when the interest rate at which it is invested multiplied by the number of years it is invested equals 72. If you invest $20,000 at an interest rate of 8%, how many years will it take for your money to double to $40,000?

32. Suppose that you get in a taxi and you see the following fare schedule:

    $2.30 plus $0.50 per mile

    How much will you pay to go ten miles?

33. A bowling handicap is a number you add to your score so you can compete fairly with more experienced bowlers. To find your handicap, subtract your average score for the last three games from 200. Then multiply that number by 0.80 (this takes 80% of the number). The result is your bowling handicap. Suppose your average for the last three games was 110. Calculate your handicap.

ANSWERS

31. The answer is 9. You get this by asking yourself the question, "What would I have to multiply by 8 in order to get 72?" You do not actually use the $40,000 or the $20,000. They are in the problem in order to show how the money doubles.

32. The taxi ride costs $7.30 based on adding $2.30 to $5.00. To find the $5.00, multiply ten miles by the $0.50 cost per mile.

33. The bowling handicap is 72. When you subtract 110 from 200, you get 90. Multiplying the 90 by 0.8 gives 72.

WHOLE NUMBER PROBLEMS

Most of the problems on the GED use whole numbers. For this reason, most of the instruction and practice in this book use only whole numbers. Fortunately, this kind of problem is the type that people feel most comfortable with.

FRACTION PROBLEMS

Operations with fractions are perhaps the most annoying of mathematical operations. One reason may be a lack of practice. It is hoped that this fraction instruction section will help you to master the basics so that you do well when you see fractions on the GED.

There are essentially two types of fraction work that you must be able to do:

Type one: Multiplication and division
Type two: Addition and subtraction

A fraction is a way of splitting something up so you can see the relationship between the parts. The fraction $\frac{1}{2}$ is the most familiar of fractions; you already have an idea of what it represents.

Every fraction is made up of two parts, the numerator and the denominator. The numerator is the top of the fraction. The denominator is the bottom of the fraction. For example, in the fraction $\frac{3}{4}$, the numerator is 3 and the denominator is 4.

You can think of the numerator as the "part," while the denominator is the "whole." For example, if you say that $\frac{1}{2}$ of your money goes for rent, you are saying that for every two dollars that you have, one of these dollars goes for rent. Two dollars is the whole amount of money, and one dollar is the part that goes for rent.

34. Stock prices are given in fractions. The stock market report says that Super Sporting Goods is selling at $24\frac{1}{2}$ up $\frac{1}{4}$. The fractions are fractional parts of a dollar. In dollars and cents, what is the selling price of Super Sporting Goods stock? In dollars and cents, how much has it gone up? What was the previous selling price? Stock prices also are given in eighths. How many cents is an eighth of a dollar?

ANSWERS

34. The selling price is $24.50 (since half of a dollar is 50 cents). The stock has gone up 25 cents (a quarter of a dollar). The previous selling price was $24.25. Because $24.50 is a quarter higher than the price used to be, subtract a quarter to obtain $24.25. An eighth of a dollar is $12\frac{1}{2}$ cents. To find this, divide $1.00 by 8 or divide $\frac{1}{4}$ dollar ($0.25) by 2.

MULTIPLICATION AND DIVISION OF FRACTIONS

These two operations are the easiest fraction operations, and they work basically alike.

Multiplication

- Multiply the tops (numerators); then write the answer as the new numerator.
- Multiply the bottoms (denominators); then write the answer as the new denominator.
- Reduce the result if necessary.

EXAMPLE

In the product $\left(\frac{2}{3}\right)\left(\frac{3}{4}\right)$,

$2 \times 3 = 6$, the new numerator
$3 \times 4 = 12$, the new denominator
$\frac{6}{12} = \frac{1}{2}$, the new fraction

Multiply the following fractions:

35. $\frac{3}{5} \times \frac{2}{3}$

36. $\frac{1}{4} \times \frac{3}{4}$

37. $\frac{5}{7} \times \frac{1}{3}$

38. $\frac{1}{3} \times \frac{1}{4}$

ANSWERS

35. $\frac{2}{5}$ 36. $\frac{3}{16}$ 37. $\frac{5}{21}$ 38. $\frac{1}{12}$

Division

To divide fractions, first take the second fraction (the divisor) and turn it upside down. This process is called inverting the fraction. Then multiply the two fractions.

EXAMPLE

What is $\frac{1}{8}$ divided by $\frac{3}{4}$?

$\frac{1}{8} \div \frac{3}{4} = \frac{1}{8} \times \frac{4}{3}$ (This is the "invert and multiply" step.)

The numerator is $1 \times 4 = 4$.
The denominator is $8 \times 3 = 24$.

The new fraction is $\frac{4}{24}$.

Both 4 and 24 can be divided by 4 (reduced), so the answer is $\frac{1}{6}$.

39. $\frac{2}{3} \div \frac{1}{3}$

40. $\dfrac{3}{4} \div \dfrac{1}{5}$

41. $\dfrac{4}{5} \div \dfrac{2}{3}$

42. $\dfrac{5}{9} \div \dfrac{2}{3}$

ANSWERS

39. **2**   40. $\dfrac{\mathbf{15}}{\mathbf{4}}$ 41. $\dfrac{\mathbf{6}}{\mathbf{5}}$ 42. $\dfrac{\mathbf{5}}{\mathbf{6}}$

ADDITION AND SUBTRACTION OF FRACTIONS

The reason that adding and subtracting are more difficult than multiplying and dividing is that there is often an extra step before you can add and subtract. This initial step is to change both of the fractions so that they have the same, or common, denominator. There are several ways to do this, but the most reliable way is to multiply the existing denominators together to get the new one.

EXAMPLE

What is $\dfrac{1}{5} + \dfrac{1}{3}$?

The new denominator is 5(3) = 15.
The way to find the new numerator of each fraction is to divide the original denominator into the new denominator, and then multiply the result by the old numerator.

$$15 \div 5 = 3, \text{ so } \dfrac{1}{5} = \dfrac{3(1)}{15} = \dfrac{3}{15}$$

$$15 \div 3 = 5, \text{ so } \dfrac{1}{3} = \dfrac{5(1)}{15} = \dfrac{5}{15}$$

After you have rewritten both fractions so that they each have the same denominator, the problem is easy. You add (or subtract) the numerators and leave the denominators alone.

$$\dfrac{1}{5} + \dfrac{1}{3} = \dfrac{3}{15} + \dfrac{5}{15} = \dfrac{3+5}{15} = \dfrac{8}{15}$$

Add or subtract the following fractions. Remember to change them first so that they have the same denominator.

43. $\dfrac{5}{6} + \dfrac{2}{3}$

44. $\dfrac{2}{3} - \dfrac{1}{8}$

45. $\dfrac{7}{8} + \dfrac{3}{4}$

46. $\dfrac{6}{7} - \dfrac{1}{3}$

ANSWERS

43. $\dfrac{\mathbf{3}}{\mathbf{2}}$ 44. $\dfrac{\mathbf{13}}{\mathbf{24}}$ 45. $\dfrac{\mathbf{13}}{\mathbf{8}}$ 46. $\dfrac{\mathbf{11}}{\mathbf{21}}$

IMPROPER FRACTIONS

Sometimes a fraction has a numerator that is greater than the denominator. This is called an improper fraction. Improper fractions should be rewritten as a mixed number (a whole number plus a proper fraction). To do this, divide the denominator into the numerator, and then write this number followed by the remainder placed over the original denominator.

EXAMPLE

Write $\dfrac{15}{12}$ as a mixed number.

You can tell that it is improper because the top is greater than the bottom.
The first step is to see if the fraction can be reduced. Since both numbers can be divided by 3, the fraction reduces to $\dfrac{5}{4}$.

Dividing the 4 into the 5 gives 1 with 1 left over, so $\frac{15}{12} = \frac{5}{4} = 1\frac{1}{4}$.

PRACTICE

Change the following improper fractions into mixed numbers:

47. $\frac{11}{9}$

48. $\frac{9}{8}$

49. $\frac{27}{8}$

50. $\frac{18}{7}$

ANSWERS

47. $1\frac{2}{9}$ 48. $1\frac{1}{8}$ 49. $3\frac{3}{8}$ 50. $2\frac{4}{7}$

DECIMALS

Decimals are nearly as easy to deal with as are whole numbers.

ADDITION AND SUBTRACTION OF DECIMALS

The only thing you need to remember when operating with decimals is to line up the problems so that the decimal points are in a straight line. Then, go about the problem just as you would do if there were no decimals. The decimal point in the answer goes straight below the decimal points in the problem.

EXAMPLE

What is 34.765 – 2.33?

Line up the problem like this:
Then subtract, bringing the
decimal point straight down.

$$\begin{array}{r} 34.765 \\ -\ 2.33 \\ \hline 32.435 \end{array}$$

PRACTICE

Add or subtract the following decimals:

51. 4.005 + 98.8

52. 1.23 – 0.9

53. 1002.15 – 3.4

54. 17.67 + 5.0004

ANSWERS

51. **102.805**
52. **0.33**
53. **998.75**
54. **22.6704**

MULTIPLICATION OF DECIMALS

When multiplying decimal numbers, multiply as though there were no decimals. To determine where the decimal point goes in the answer, first count the number of places to the right of the decimal point in both of the numbers you are multiplying. Then find the sum of these decimal places, and position the decimal point that many places in from the right-hand end of the product.

EXAMPLE

What is 23.004 × 3.45?

When you multiply as if there were no decimals, you get 7936380.

```
    23.004
  ×  3.45
   115020
   920160
  6901200
  7936380
```

In all, there are 5 decimal places to the right of the decimal, so move the decimal point in 5 places from the right-hand end, giving 79.36380.

PRACTICE

Multiply the following decimal numbers:

55. 23.55 × 14.1

56. 1.333 × 25.002

57. 0.0044 × 35.4

58. 20,000 × 0.005

ANSWERS

55. **332.055**
56. **33.327666**
57. **0.15576**
58. **100**

DIVISION OF DECIMALS

When you divide and there are decimal numbers involved, look at the divisor (the 3.45 in the example below) and move the decimal point to the right however many places necessary for the divisor to be a whole number. Then move the decimal point in the dividend (the 150.9375 in the example) the same number of places that you moved the other decimal point. Next, divide as if there were no decimals. Finally, place the decimal point in the quotient (the answer line) directly above the decimal point in the dividend.

EXAMPLE

What is 150.9375 ÷ 3.45?

You must move the decimal point 2 places to make 3.45 the whole number 345, so move the decimal point in 150.9375 2 places to the right also, and then divide.

```
              43.75
  345)15093.75
      1380
      129375
      1035
       25875
       2415
        1725
        1725
           0
```

PRACTICE

Divide the following decimal numbers:

59. 198.34 ÷ 8.44

60. 1.4 ÷ 0.0056

61. 2.0091 ÷ 2,009.1

62. 69.084 ÷ 34.2

ANSWERS

59. **23.5**
60. **250**
61. **0.001**
62. **2.02**

SEQUENCING

There will be questions on the GED exam that ask you to arrange numbers in order from smallest to largest or from largest to smallest. Obviously, this is not hard if you are dealing with whole numbers. When you are working with fractions or decimals, the job is a little more difficult, so some practice is in order.

SEQUENCING OF FRACTIONS

If the denominators (bottoms) are the same, then the sequencing is just what you would imagine. That is, in placing the fractions $\frac{2}{7}$, $\frac{6}{7}$, and $\frac{4}{7}$ in order from smallest to largest, the smallest is $\frac{2}{7}$, the next is $\frac{4}{7}$, and the last is $\frac{6}{7}$.

If the denominators are not the same, then you must first rewrite all of the fractions so that their denominators are the same. To do this, follow the same process that you practiced in the addition of fractions section earlier in this chapter.

EXAMPLE

Arrange the fractions $\frac{5}{8}$, $\frac{3}{4}$, and $\frac{2}{3}$ in sequence from smallest to largest.

To find a common denominator, multiply the denominators 8 and 3 to obtain 24. In this case, you don't have to multiply by the denominator 4 because it will divide into any denominator into which 8 divides.

$$\frac{5}{8} = \frac{15}{24} \qquad \frac{3}{4} = \frac{18}{24} \qquad \frac{2}{3} = \frac{16}{24}$$

Placing these numbers in order gives $\frac{15}{24}$, $\frac{16}{24}$, $\frac{18}{24}$, so the original fractions in order are $\frac{5}{8}$, $\frac{2}{3}$, $\frac{3}{4}$.

SEQUENCING OF DECIMALS

Decimals are easier to sequence than are fractions. To do so, add enough zeros so that every number has the same number of digits to the right of the decimal point. Then you can mentally remove the decimal point.

EXAMPLE

Organize the numbers 0.004, 0.15, 0.22, and 0.05 from smallest to largest.

Adding zeros to give every number the same number of digits to the right of the decimal point gives the following:

0.004   0.150   0.220   0.050

When you mentally remove the decimal point, you can see that the numbers fit into sequence as follows:

0.004   0.050   0.150   0.220

PRACTICE

Arrange the following numbers in sequence from smallest to largest:

63. $\frac{3}{8}$ $\qquad$ $\frac{2}{5}$ $\qquad$ $\frac{1}{2}$

64. 0.0335 $\qquad$ 0.120 $\qquad$ 0.0055

65. $\frac{7}{8}$ $\qquad$ $\frac{3}{4}$ $\qquad$ $\frac{11}{16}$

66. 0.002 $\qquad$ 0.004 $\qquad$ 0.010

ANSWERS

63. $\frac{3}{8}, \frac{2}{5}, \frac{1}{2}$ **(They are in order.)**

64. **0.0055, 0.0335, 0.120**

65. $\frac{11}{16}, \frac{3}{4}, \frac{7}{8}$

66. **0.002, 0.004, 0.010 (They are in order.)**

End of Chapter Practice

For problems 1–28, perform the indicated operation:

1. 23 × 105

2. $\frac{1}{2} + \frac{3}{8}$

3. 405 + 1,009

4. $\dfrac{458.67}{100}$

5. $\dfrac{3}{8} \times \dfrac{2}{3}$

6. $\dfrac{5}{8} \div \dfrac{1}{2}$

7. $\dfrac{625}{25}$

8. $\dfrac{1}{2} - \dfrac{1}{3}$

9. $51 - 19$

10. 203×500

11. 1.01×3.5

12. $\dfrac{2}{3} + \dfrac{1}{6}$

13. $\dfrac{135}{9}$

14. $29.13 + 19.005$

15. 3.275×100

16. $130 - 0.095$

17. $20 + 159,917$

18. $\dfrac{7}{8} \div \dfrac{1}{3}$

19. 0.005×150

20. $\dfrac{3}{4} - \dfrac{3}{8}$

21. 75.05×0.15

22. $13 \times 1,000$

23. $\dfrac{5}{8} \times \dfrac{3}{4}$

24. $\dfrac{3}{4} \div \dfrac{1}{2}$

25. $95.6 - 0.75$

26. $34,974 \div 1,000$

27. $23,000 - 651$

28. $15.015 + 3.9$

For problems 29–32 arrange the numbers from smallest to largest:

29. $\dfrac{1}{4}, \dfrac{1}{3}, \dfrac{1}{6}$

30. $0.05, 0.005, 0.15$

31. $0.0005, 0.02, 0.001$

32. $\dfrac{5}{8}, \dfrac{2}{3}, \dfrac{3}{4}$

ANSWERS

1. **2,415**
2. $\frac{7}{8}$
3. **1,414**
4. **4.5867**
5. $\frac{1}{4}$
6. $\frac{5}{4}$, **or** $1\frac{1}{4}$
7. **25**
8. $\frac{1}{6}$
9. **32**
10. **101,500**
11. **3.535**
12. $\frac{5}{6}$
13. **15**
14. **48.135**
15. **327.5**
16. **129.905**

17. **159,937**
18. $\frac{21}{8}$, **or** $2\frac{5}{8}$
19. **0.75**
20. $\frac{3}{8}$
21. **11.2575**
22. **13,000**
23. $\frac{15}{32}$
24. $\frac{3}{2}$, **or** $1\frac{1}{2}$
25. **94.85**
26. **34.974**
27. **22,349**
28. **18.915**
29. $\frac{1}{6}, \frac{1}{4}, \frac{1}{3}$
30. **0.005, 0.05, 0.15**
31. **0.0005, 0.001, 0.02**
32. $\frac{5}{8}, \frac{2}{3}, \frac{3}{4}$ **(They are in order.)**

Algebra

4

Algebra is a skill that you already use, most likely without realizing it. For example, you are doing algebra any time you are thinking about an everyday problem and you are looking for a number. In algebra we call this number the "unknown," and often represent it by the letter x, although any letter will do. For example, suppose you are wondering what percent of your income you pay in taxes. If you know how much money you make in a year and the dollar amount of your tax, you can set up an algebra equation that looks like this:

$$(x\%)(\text{total income}) = \text{tax}$$

Solving this equation for x will give your tax percentage.

Translation

The word "translation" in algebra means taking one or more sentences and using the ideas in these sentences to write an equation. For example, suppose you know that you have 25 decorator items to sell and you need to make $500. You want to find out what your selling price should be, so you think:

$$(25)(\$x) = \$500$$

This is translating from a sentence to an equation. The x could be any letter, but x is the one frequently used. The x is called a *variable*, because it can vary, or change. For example, if you decide to set the price so that you can make $600, the equation becomes the following:

$$(25)(\$x) = \$600$$

Using x to represent the unknown is often expressed in this form:

$$\text{"Let } x = \text{"}$$

In this example we are saying, "Let x = the selling price of each item."

PRACTICE

For each of the following, write an equation using x or any other letter. Do not attempt to solve the equation or "get an answer." Writing an equation is your goal.

1. If Sue had twice the income she presently makes, she would be making $82,000 a year.

2. The recipe for cinnamon rolls calls for $\frac{2}{3}$ cup of brown sugar. If the recipe were to be tripled, what would the brown sugar amount be?

3. Write an equation that describes the distance traveled if the first leg of the journey is twice as long as the second leg and the third leg is 50 miles less than the first.

4. Write an equation that describes the calorie intake for a fast food meal for which the hamburger has twice the calories of the medium drink, and the small fries have the same calorie count as the drink.

5. The clue in a mystery describes a street address by saying that the second digit is twice the first digit, and that the third digit is one bigger than the second.

6. The average teen's weekly paycheck is $250 less than the average adult's paycheck.

7. The distance around the base paths on a baseball diamond is 4 times the distance from home to first base.

ANSWERS

1. **2x = $82,000**
2. $3\left(\dfrac{2}{3}\right) = x$
3. **First leg = 2x**
   Second leg = x
   Third leg = 2x – 50
   Distance = (2x) + (x) + (2x – 50)
4. **Hamburger calories= 2x**
   Drink calories = x
   Fries calories = x
   Total meal calories = 2x + x + x
5. **First digit = x**
   Second digit = 2x
   Third digit = 2x + 1
   Address = x, 2x, 2x + 1
6. **Adult paycheck = x**
   Teen paycheck = x – 250
7. **Let x = distance from home to first.**
   Then 4x = distance around all the bases.

Signed Numbers

Numbers are either positive or negative. You have had experience with this idea in many areas of your life. Some examples of negative numbers are an overdrawn bank account, a cold snap with temperatures below zero, and the national debt.

Positive numbers include the amount of money that dinner costs, the measurement of a carpet, or your shoe size. Many people find that the idea of signed numbers can best be understood by thinking of a number line, as shown below.

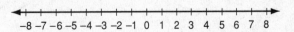

Notice that the positive numbers get larger as you move to the right of zero. The negative numbers also get larger as you move to the right toward zero.

USING SIGNED NUMBERS

ADDITION

You can picture solving the equation –3 + 4 = ? by looking at the number line below.

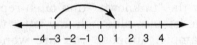

Start at the location of –3 and go 4 spaces in the positive direction, because adding a positive number means to go in the positive direction. You will land at the location marked 1, so the solution is –3 + 4 = 1.

SUBTRACTION

If you saw the subtraction problem 1 – (–4) = ?, you could use this easy system:

An odd number of minuses multiplied together is a minus.

An even number of minuses multiplied together is a plus.

So, the problem becomes 1 + 4 = 5.

Now that you have dealt with the multiplication of negative numbers (minuses), you are ready to move along the number line. Start at 1 and move 4 spaces in the positive direction. You are now at 5, your answer.

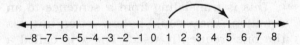

PRACTICE

Add or subtract the following numbers:

8. 5 + (– 2)

9. 6 – (– 2)

10. 9 – (4)

11. –7 – 7

12. –12 + 1

13. 6 – (–3)

14. –5 – (–1)

15. 0 – (–9)

ANSWERS

8. **3**	12. **–11**
9. **8**	13. **9**
10. **5**	14. **–4**
11. **–14**	15. **9**

MULTIPLICATION AND DIVISION

To multiply or divide two signed numbers, just do the operation as though there were no pluses or minuses present. Then use the following rules:

The sign of the answer will be + if the signs are the same.

The sign of the answer will be – if the signs are different.

EXAMPLES

(6)(4) = 24
(6)(–4) = –24
(–6)(–4) = 24

PRACTICE

16. (–5)(–3)

17. $\dfrac{12}{-6}$

18. $\dfrac{-15}{5}$

19. (–6)(–12)

20. (–4)(2)

21. $\dfrac{(8)}{-2}$

22. $\dfrac{(-4)}{(-4)}$

23. (8)(–2)

ANSWERS

16. **15**	18. **–3**	20. **–8**	22. **1**	23. **–16**
17. **–2**	19. **72**	21 **–4**		

Exponents

In the expression a^2, the 2 is called an exponent. It tells you how many times to multiply *a by itself* (not by 2). For example, 2^3 means:

$$2 \times 2 \times 2 = 8$$

EXAMPLES

$a^2 = (a)(a)$
$x^3 = (x)(x)(x)$
$3^4 = (3)(3)(3)(3)$

PRACTICE

Find the following powers:

24. 2^5

25. 4^3

Write each of the following without an exponent:

26. x^4

27. c^6

ANSWERS

24. **32**
25. **64**
26. $(x)(x)(x)(x)$
27. $(c)(c)(c)(c)(c)(c)$

USING EXPONENTS WHEN MULTIPLYING

When there are exponents involved in multiplying numbers or variables that are alike, add the exponents.

EXAMPLES

$(a^2)(a^3) = a^{2+3} = a^5$
$(x)(x^2) = x^{1+2} = x^3$
$(2b)(3b^2) = 2(3)(b)(b^2) = 6b^{1+2} = 6b^3$
Note: $3b^2 \neq (3b)^2$

USING EXPONENTS WHEN DIVIDING

The process used when dividing numbers or variables with exponents is like multiplying, but you subtract the exponents instead of adding them. Always subtract the denominator exponent from the numerator exponent.

EXAMPLES

$$\frac{a^5}{a^2} = a^{5-2} = a^3$$

$$\frac{a^3}{a^5} = a^{3-5} = a^{-2}$$

$$\frac{6x^3}{2x} = \frac{6}{2}\left(\frac{x^3}{x}\right) = 3x^{3-1} = 3x^2$$

USING EXPONENTS WHEN ADDING AND SUBTRACTING

The only time you can add or subtract when using exponents is when the letters or numbers that have the exponents are alike, and the exponents are the same.

That is, because $2x^2$ and $3x^2$ both have the exponent 2 applied to x, you can add them:

$$2x^2 + 3x^2 = (2 + 3)x^2 = 5x^2$$

Notice that the x^2 does not change.

This is rather like adding 2 apples and 3 apples. You add the numbers, and the word apples does not change.

But you *cannot* do the following addition:

$$2x^3 + 3x^2$$

You cannot add because the exponents differ.

PRACTICE

28. $(x^2)(x^4)$

29. $(2^3)(3^2)$

30. $\dfrac{(x^5)}{(x^2)}$

31. $(4x)(3x^3)$

32. $\dfrac{(18y^3)}{(6y)}$

33. $6x^5 - 2x^5$

34. $7a^2 + a^3$

35. $\dfrac{5d^2}{5d^7}$

28. x^6
29. $(8)(9) = 72$
30. x^3
31. $12x^4$
32. $3y^2$
33. $4x^5$
34. **Cannot be simplified further. Remember that you can add or subtract only when the exponents are the same.**
35. d^{-5}

Scientific Notation

Scientific notation is a way of writing numbers. For example, $3{,}217 = 3.217 \times 10^3$, that is, $3{,}217 \times 10^3$ is the number 3,217 written in scientific notation. They are the same number, just written differently. As you read the examples below, notice three things:

1. The decimal in the scientific notation number is between the first two digits. This is always true.
2. The exponent with the 10 tells how many spaces to move the decimal in order to return to the original number.
3. The sign of the exponent tells which *direction* to move the decimal in order to return to the original number. A positive exponent means to move the decimal in the positive, or right-hand, direction. A negative exponent means to move the decimal in the negative, or left-hand, direction.

EXAMPLES

$741 = 7.41 \times 10^2$

$47{,}900 = 4.79 \times 10^4$ The zeroes past the 9 may be dropped or kept.

$0.015 = 1.5 \times 10^{-2}$

$4.5 \times 10^4 = 45{,}000$ You need to add zeroes here in order to be able to move the decimal four spaces.

$6.97 \times 10^{-2} = 0.0697$

Write the following numbers in scientific notation:

36. 795

37. 46

38. 90,845

39. 0.082

40. 0.00091

41. 1,003

Write the following scientific notation numbers in ordinary form:

42. 4.05×10^3

43. 7.96×10^{-1}

44. 8.04×10^5

45. 9.00×10^{-2}

46. 3.75×10^4

36. **7.95×10^2**
37. **4.6×10**
38. **9.0845×10^4**
39. **8.2×10^{-2}**
40. **9.1×10^{-4}**
41. **1.003×10^3**
42. **4,050**
43. **0.796**
44. **804,000**

45. **0.0900**
46. **37,500**

Order of Operations

When working math problems of any kind, there is a certain order of operations. This means that there is a sequence that you must follow in order to get the correct answer. The proper sequence follows:

1. Work within parentheses first, observing within the parentheses the order shown in steps 2 and 3 below.
2. Perform each multiplication and division in order from left to right.
3. Perform each addition and subtraction in order from left to right.

PRACTICE

Find each of the following using the order of operations:

47. $5 + 9 \times 3 + 7$

48. $12 \div 3 + 4 \times 6$

49. $4 (9 + 3) - 6 \times 7$

50. $18 - 9 + 5 \times 2$

51. $20 \div 4 - 6 + (3 - 1)$

52. $(144 \div 3)(4 - 6)$

ANSWERS

47. **39** 49. **6**   50. **19** 51. **1**   52. **–96**
48. **28**

Solving Equations

To solve an equation means to get the variable (like x) on one side of the equals sign and everything else on the other side of the equals sign. In order to do this, you have to move numbers around. Remember this rule:

RULE: Whenever you do something on one side of the equals sign, you must do exactly the same thing on the other side of the equals sign.

For example, look below at the solution of the equation $x + 7 = 3$:

$$x + 7 = 3$$
$$-7 = -7$$
$$x = -4$$

The 7 was subtracted in order to get the x to be alone. The 7 was subtracted from both sides because of the rule above.

Hint: Whenever you have to "move" a number in an equation, you are actually canceling out the number. To do this, you have to perform the opposite arithmetic. For example, if the problem says to add, you must subtract; if it says to subtract, you add. If the problem says to multiply, you divide; and if it says to divide, you multiply.

As you study the examples, try to see how the variable is isolated in each case.

EXAMPLE

$3x = 15$ In this case, $3x$ means that 3 is multiplied by x. In order to get x by itself, you would divide by 3. Remember that you have to divide both sides by 3.

$$\frac{3x}{3} = \frac{15}{3}$$

$x = 5$ The solution is $x = 5$; that is, the original equation is true when x is 5.

EXAMPLE

$x + 15 = 60$ In order to isolate x, you need to get rid of the 15. Since it has an addition sign in front of it, the reverse is subtraction, so subtract 15 from both sides.

$$\begin{aligned} x + 15 &= 60 \\ -15 &= -15 \\ x &= 45 \end{aligned}$$

The solution is $x = 45$; that is, the original equation is true when x is 45.

EXAMPLE

Sometimes solving an equation is a two-step process.

$2x + 5 = 23$ The first step is to get rid of the number (5) that is not with the x.

$$\begin{aligned} -5 &= -5 \\ 2x &= 18 \end{aligned}$$

$\dfrac{2x}{2} = \dfrac{18}{2}$ The second step is to divide both sides by 2 to get x by itself.

$x = 9$ The original equation is true when $x = 9$.

PRACTICE

For each of the following equations, find the value of the letter (variable):

53. $x + 15 = 32$

54. $5x + 6 = 10$

55. $120 = 2x + x$

56. $3x + 4x - 5 = 23$

57. $2x - 4 = -12$

58. $3(x + 2) = 15$

59. $12(c - 12) = 10 + c$

60. $15 = \dfrac{t}{5}$

ANSWERS

53. **17**
54. $\dfrac{4}{5}$
55. **40; Your first step in any solution is to combine what you can. In this case that would be to add the $2x$ and x to get $120 = 3x$.**
56. **4**
57. **−4**
58. **3**
59. **14**
60. **75**

Percent

The idea of percent logically follows solving equations.

The basic percent equation looks like this:

$$\% = \frac{\text{part} \times 100}{\text{whole}}$$

Since there are three unknown quantities in this equation (%, part, and whole), the unknown can go in any one of these three positions. Any percent problem will then fit one of these formats:

When looking for %:

$$x = \frac{\text{part}(100)}{\text{whole}}$$

When looking for the part:

$$\% = \frac{(x)(100)}{\text{whole}}$$

When looking for the whole:

$$\% = \frac{\text{part}(100)}{x}$$

EXAMPLE

If you scored 60 out of a possible 80 on a test, what is your percent score?

$$\% = \frac{\text{part} \times 100}{\text{whole}}$$

$$\% = \frac{60 \times 100}{80}$$

$$\% = 75$$

Your percent score is 75%.

EXAMPLE

Stan paid 5% sales tax on a sound system. The sales tax was $60. What was the purchase price of the sound system?

$$5\% = \frac{\$60 \times 100}{\text{price of whole system}}$$

$$(5)(\text{price}) = 6000$$

$$\frac{(5)(\text{price})}{5} = \frac{6000}{5}$$

$$\text{price} = \frac{6000}{5}$$

$$\text{price} = 1200$$

The purchase price was $1,200.

EXAMPLE

If a car dealer requires a 15% down payment, what would that cost you on a $20,000 car?

$$\% = \frac{\text{part} \times 100}{\text{whole}}$$

$$15\% = \frac{x \text{ dollars} \times 100}{\$20,000}$$

$$\frac{(15)(20,000)}{1} = \left(\frac{(x)(100)}{20,000}\right)\left(\frac{20,000}{1}\right)$$

$$(15)(20,000) = 100x$$

$$300,000 = 100x$$

$$\frac{300,000}{100} = \frac{100x}{100}$$

$$3,000 = x$$

You must make a $3,000 down payment.

PRACTICE

61. What is 30% of 1,200?

62. What percent is 12 out of 15?

63. If 5% of your salary is $60, how much is your salary?

64. If you finished 4 hours of your 12 hour work shift, what % is finished?

65. Jane gets an 8% good driver discount on car insurance. If her insurance is normally $1,000 a year, how much is the discount?

66. A freeze-damaged fruit shipment has 200 bad grapefruit. If 10% of the fruit was damaged, how many grapefruit were there before the freeze?

ANSWERS

61. **360**
62. **80%**
63. **$1,200**
64. **$33\frac{1}{3}$%**
65. **$80**
66. **2,000**

Proportion

A proportion is an equation that equates two ratios. You can recognize a proportion by its form, which looks like this:

$$\frac{A}{B} = \frac{C}{D}$$

It is hard to avoid using proportions in everyday life, whether you are cooking, traveling, building, figuring your pay, or doing any number of other activities.

CROSS MULTIPLYING

The process called cross multiplying can help you solve proportions quickly. To cross multiply, you multiply and equate the parts of the proportion that are diagonally opposite. Look at the following proportion:

$$\frac{A}{B} \diagdown \frac{C}{D}$$

Because *A* and *D* are diagonally opposite and *B* and *C* are diagonally opposite, multiply and equate each pair:

$$AD = BC$$

You can then solve as before for whatever quantity that you want to find.

EXAMPLE

Solve the equation for *x*.

$$\frac{12}{4} = \frac{9}{x}$$

Cross multiply to solve for *x*:

$12x = (9)(4)$
$12x = 36$
$x = 3$ (Divide both sides by 12.)

PRACTICE

Solve each of the following equations for the variable (letter):

67. $\dfrac{x}{15} = \dfrac{2}{5}$

68. $\dfrac{3}{4} = \dfrac{6}{a}$

69. $\dfrac{7}{3b} = \dfrac{3}{9}$

70. $\dfrac{2}{5} = \dfrac{c}{41}$

71. $\dfrac{x}{-3} = \dfrac{12}{4}$

72. $\dfrac{12}{2y} = \dfrac{-3}{5}$

ANSWERS

67. **6**　69. **7**　70. $\mathbf{16\dfrac{2}{5}}$　71. **–9**　72. **–10**
68. **8**

SETTING UP A PROPORTION

Suppose that you are mixing lemonade mix and water for a large group. You know that your usual recipe is to use 3 scoops of lemonade mix for each quart of water. If you want to know how many scoops you need for 12 quarts, you can set up the following proportions:

$$\frac{3 \text{ scoops}}{1 \text{ quart}} = \frac{x \text{ scoops}}{12 \text{ quarts}}$$

Notice that in setting up the proportion there is a logical order. Both numerators are about scoops. Both denominators are about quarts. The left side of the equation is about your usual recipe. The right side of the equation is about the larger recipe. When you set up proportions, use this type of logic.

Using the cross multiplying technique to solve this proportion gives:

$$(3)(12) = (1)(x)$$
$$36 = x$$

PRACTICE

For each of the following problems, set up a proportion and then solve for the unknown:

73. If you are supposed to give 5 milligrams of antibiotic to a 15 pound dog, how many milligrams would you give to a 51 pound dog?

74. If you drive at a constant speed and can cover 100 miles in 2 hours, how many miles can you cover in $3\frac{1}{2}$ hours?

75. Your neighbor gets nice results by using 3 bags of grass seed on his 10,000 square feet of lawn. How many bags would you need for a 15,000 square foot lawn?

76. Rick used 20 gallons of gasoline for a 710 mile trip. At that same rate, how many gallons will it take for a 500 mile trip?

77. Don's friend joined an investment club. He invested $5,000 and earned a profit of $800 the first year. Don would like to invest $12,000. What would his profit be at the same rate?

ANSWERS

73. $\dfrac{5 \text{ mg}}{15 \text{ lb}} = \dfrac{x \text{ mg}}{51 \text{ lb}}$; **17**

74. $\dfrac{100 \text{ mi}}{2 \text{ h}} = \dfrac{x \text{ mi}}{3\frac{1}{2} \text{ h}}$; **175**

75. $\dfrac{3 \text{ bags}}{10,000 \text{ sq ft}} = \dfrac{x \text{ bags}}{15,000 \text{ sq ft}}$; **4.5**

76. $\dfrac{20 \text{ gal}}{710 \text{ mi}} = \dfrac{x \text{ gal}}{500 \text{ mi}}$; **about 14** $\left(\dfrac{1,000}{71}\right)$

77. $\dfrac{\$800}{\$5,000} = \dfrac{\$x}{\$12,000}$; **$1,920**

Formulas

A formula is a way of describing how things are related to each other. For example, here is a formula you might use when driving a car:

$$\text{Distance} = \text{Rate times Time}$$
$$\text{or}$$
$$\text{D} = \text{R} \times \text{T}$$

HOW TO WORK FORMULA PROBLEMS

Step 1: Write the formula.
Step 2: Directly under each letter, write a number for that letter, if you know one. If you do not know, write the letter itself. This will be the unknown for which you will be solving.
Step 3: Solve the equation that you have now written.

EXAMPLE

How long would it take to drive 600 miles at an average speed of 50 miles per hour?

Step 1: Distance = Rate × Time
Step 2: 600 miles = 50 × T
Step 3: Solve for T.

$$600 = 50T$$
$$\frac{600}{50} = \frac{50T}{50}$$
$$12 = T$$

It would take 12 hours.

PRACTICE

78. How much interest will you pay to borrow $15,000 for a year at a rate of 9% ? (Remember that 9% will become .09 when you use it in a problem.)

$$\text{Principal} \times \text{Rate} = \text{Interest}$$
$$\text{or}$$
$$P \times R = I$$

79. If you had a Christmas tree lot, what price would you need to charge for each tree if you had 75 trees to sell and wanted to make $3,000? The business formula is shown below.

Cost (also called income) = number × rate

80. Using the formula for the area of a triangle ($A = \frac{1}{2}bh$), find the area of a triangle whose base is 12 feet long and whose height is 5 feet.

ANSWERS

78. **$1,350**
79. **$40**
80. **30 sq. ft.**

Substitution

Substitution is like working with a formula, because you are writing numbers to replace letters.

EXAMPLE

Solve $2a^2 + b - 3c$, given that $a = 3$, $b = 4$, and $c = 2$.

As in the formula problem, write known numbers for the letters and then simplify.

$$2a^2 + b - 3c = 2(3)^2 + 4 - 3(2)$$
$$= 2(9) + 4 - 6$$
$$= 18 + 4 - 6$$
$$= 22 - 6$$
$$= 16$$

PRACTICE

81. What is the value of $2a^2b^3$ if: $a = 2$ and $b = 3$?

82. What is the value of $2(x^2 - y^2) + 3z$ if $x = 5$, $y = 4$, and $z = 3$?

ANSWERS

81. **216**   82. **27**

Factoring

You already know how to factor, though you may not have called it that. For example, when you think of the numbers that you can multiply to get 12 and you come up with 3 and 4, you have just factored. That is, you have decided that 3 and 4 are factors of 12 because they multiply together to get 12. If you were asked for another set of factors for 12, you could come up with 6 and 2 or 12 and 1.

EXAMPLE

Factor $6x^2$.

One possible factorization is $(3x)(2x)$, since $(3x)(2x) = 6x^2$.

Another possible factorization is $(6x)(x)$, whose product is also $6x^2$. There are also other factorizations that give the product $6x^2$.

EXAMPLE

Factor $18a^3$.

One posssible factorization is $(9a^2)(2a)$, since $(9a^2)(2a) = 18a^3$.

Two other factorizations are $(6a^2)(3a)$ and $(6a)(3a^2)$. There are also other factorizations that give the product $18a^3$.

PRACTICE

Find at least one set of two factors for each of the following expressions:

83. $16a^2$

84. $9r^3$

85. $21x^2y$

86. $15x^2$

83. **(8a)(2a); Other possibilities include (4a)(4a) and (16a)(a).**
84. **(3r)(3r^2); Other possibilities include (9r)(r^2) and (9r^2)(r).**
85. **(7x)(3xy); Other possibilities include (3x^2)(7y) and (7x^2)(3y).**
86. **(5x)(3x); Other possibilities include (15x)(x) and (3)(5x^2).**

FOIL AND FACTORING

THE FOIL METHOD

The FOIL method allows you to multiply expressions like $(x + 2)(x - 1)$ or $(2 - 3a)(1 + a)$ quickly. The word FOIL comes from the first letters of four words:

$$F = First$$
$$O = Outside$$
$$I = Inside$$
$$L = Last$$

These words are position words. For example, look at the product $(3a + 2)(4a - 5)$.

First: The $3a$ and the $4a$ are first in each set of parentheses.
Outside: The $3a$ and the -5 are the two outside terms.
Inside: The 2 and the $4a$ are the two inside (middle) terms.
Last: The 2 and the -5 are last in each set of parentheses.

Here is how the FOIL system works: Suppose a problem says to multiply $(3a + 2)(4a - 5)$. The FOIL steps are the following:

$$F: (3a)(4a) = 12a^2$$
$$O: (3a)(-5) = -15a$$
$$I: (2)(4a) = 8a$$
$$L: (2)(-5) = -10$$

The only ones of these four expressions that can be combined are the $-15a$ and the $8a$. In general, you can combine the "O" and "I" expressions by addition. In this case their sum is $-7a$. The whole answer is written as $12a^2 - 7a - 10$.

EXAMPLE

Multiply $(2x + 4)(5x + 3)$ using FOIL.

$$F: (2x)(5x) = 10x^2$$
$$O: (2x)(3) = 6x$$
$$I: (4)(5x) = 20x$$
$$L: (4)(3) = 12$$

Combining the $6x$ and $20x$ gives $6x + 20x = 26x$.
The final answer is $10x^2 + 26x + 12$.

EXAMPLE

Multiply $(3x + 7)(2x - 3)$ using FOIL.

Hint: Try covering the rest of this example and doing the FOIL steps by yourself. Then show yourself the answers so you can see how you are doing.

$$F: (3x)(2x) = 6x^2$$
$$O: (3x)(-3) = -9x$$
$$I: (7)(2x) = 14x$$
$$L: (7)(-3) = -21$$

Combining the $-9x$ and $14x$ gives $-9x + 14x = 5x$.
The final answer is $6x^2 + 5x - 21$.

PRACTICE

Multiply each of the following:

87. $(x + 5)(2x + 7)$

88. $(3a + 7)(2a - 2)$

89. $(4t - 3)(t + 5)$

90. $(b - 9)(2b - 4)$

87. **$2x^2 + 17x + 35$**
88. **$6a^2 + 8a - 14$**
89. **$4t^2 + 17t - 15$**
90. **$2b^2 - 22b + 36$**

USING FOIL IN FACTORING

To see the relationship between FOIL and factoring remember this:

FOIL means multiplying.
FOIL: $(3a + 2)(4a - 5) = 12a^2 - 7a - 10$

Factoring means "unmultiplying."
Factoring: $12a^2 - 7a - 10 = (3a + 2)(4a - 5)$

So, when you factor expressions with three terms like $12a^2 - 7a - 10$, you are basically "un-FOIL-ing." If you think you have found a factorization, you can check yourself by using FOIL on your answer to see if it gives you the original expression. If it does not, then your solution is not right, and so you should try again.

PRACTICE

For each of the following find at least one set of factors:

91. $x^2 + 6x + 8$

92. $10x^2 + 19x + 6$

93. $6a^2 + 8a + 2$

94. $3b^2 - 10b - 8$

95. $5c^2 + 8c + 3$

96. $2x^2 + x - 10$

ANSWERS

91. $(x + 4)(x + 2)$
92. $(5x + 2)(2x + 3)$
93. $(3a + 1)(2a + 2)$ or $(6a + 2)(a + 1)$
94. $(3b + 2)(b - 4)$
95. $(5c + 3)(c + 1)$
96. $(x - 2)(2x + 5)$

Inequalities

Suppose you wanted to describe the relationship between 7 and 5. You could say that 7 is greater than 5. An algebraic way of saying this is to write $7 > 5$. The $>$ means "greater than." There is also a $<$ symbol, which means "less than." Just remember that the little end of the symbol points to the smaller value.

You can combine each of these symbols with an equals sign. The symbol $\leq$ means "less than or equal to." The symbol $\geq$ means "greater than or equal to."

EXAMPLE

Sometimes insurance companies reward good students by offering a discount if their grade point average (GPA) is a B (3.0) or better. Express this as an inequality.

The GPA must be at least 3.0, which means that it must be greater than or equal to 3.0, so use the $\geq$ symbol. The answer is GPA ≥ 3.0.

INEQUALITY GRAPHING

A number line is often used to picture the idea of inequality, as shown below.

The way to read this graph is to say it represents values greater than –2. The fact that the circle at the –2 location is an open (not shaded in) circle is important. This means that the value of –2 is not itself included.

As you look at the number line below, notice that the circle is shaded. This means that the value of the circle itself is included. This graph represents values greater than or equal to –3.

A number line can also show a range of values that is bounded on both ends. For example, if your ideal weight lies in the range from 165 to 170 pounds, you can write the range as $165 \leq w \leq 170$, and can graph it like this:

PRACTICE

For each of the following inequalities, make a number line graph:

97. $x > 8$

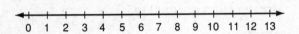

98. $a \leq -3$

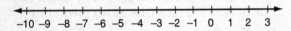

99. $t > -1$

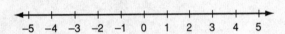

100. $x \leq 2$

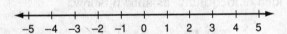

101. $1 < t < 4$

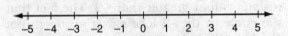

For each of the following graphs, write an inequality:

102.

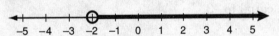

103.

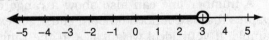

104.

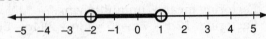

105.

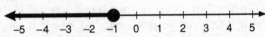

106.

107.

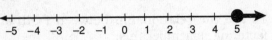

ANSWERS

97.

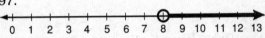

98.

99.

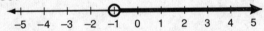

100.

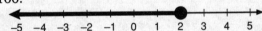

101.

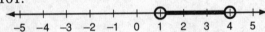

102. **$x > -2$**
103. **$x < 3$**
104. **$x \geq 5$**
105. **$-2 < x < 1$**
106. **$x \leq -1$**
107. **$-7 \leq x \leq -4$**

SOLVING INEQUALITIES

You can solve inequalities in the same way that you solve regular equations—with one exception. This exception arises when you multiply or divide by a negative number. When this happens, you must turn the inequality sign around before solving as usual. That is, a > symol becomes a < symbol, and so on.

EXAMPLE

$2x + 3 > x + 5$ This is an inequality problem. To solve it, you want to isolate the x.

$\underline{-x \qquad -x}$ The first step is to subtract x from both sides.

$x + 3 > 5$
$x + 3 > +5$
$\underline{-3 \quad -3}$ Subtract 3 from each side to isolate x.

$\qquad x > 2$ Notice that you did not multiply or divide by a negative number, so the inequality sign did not change.

The solution is all numbers that are greater than 2.

EXAMPLE

$3x + 8 > 7x - 24$ This is an inequality problem. Subtract $7x$

$\underline{-7x \qquad -7x}$
$-4x + 8 > -24$ from both sides so that the variable x is on only one side.

$-4x + 8 > -24$ Subtract 8 from both
$\underline{-8 \quad -8}$ sides to isolate x
$-4x > -32$ further.
$x < 8$ Then divide by −4 to isolate x completely.

Dividing by a negative number causes the inequality sign to reverse.

PRACTICE

Solve each of the following inequalities:

108. $x - 7 \leq 2x$

109. $3x \leq -27$

110. $9x + 2 > 20$

111. $-13r \geq 91$

112. $2c + 5 < 3c$

113. $7x - 27 \geq 4x$

114. $10 - 12a > -38$

ANSWERS

108. **$-7 \leq x$**
109. **$x \leq -9$**
110. **$x > 2$**
111. **$r \leq -7$**
112. **$5 < c$**
113. **$9 \leq x$**
114. **$a < 4$**

End of Chapter Practice

1. Simplify $4a - 6a - 3a + a$.
   (1) $10a$
   (2) $4a$
   (3) $-4a$
   (4) $-6a$
   (5) a

2. What is 3.4×10^{-5} written in ordinary form?
   (1) 0.000034
   (2) 0.00034
   (3) 0.34
   (4) 34,000
   (5) 340,000

3. What is the value of x if $\dfrac{4}{x} = \dfrac{12}{9}$?
   (1) 3
   (2) 7
   (3) 9
   (4) 18
   (5) 27

4. A teacher requests that his annual salary be paid in 12 equal payments instead of 10. If each of the 10 payments is m dollars, how many dollars will each of the 12 payments be?

   (1) $m - 3$
   (2) $\dfrac{6m}{5}$
   (3) $\dfrac{5m}{6}$
   (4) $10m - 12$
   (5) $12m - 10$

5. Solve $3x + 8 = -12 + x$ for x

   (1) -10
   (2) -2
   (3) -1
   (4) 2
   (5) 5

6. Ann buys an $18,000 car in a state with a 6% sales tax. How much will the tax be?

   (1) $108
   (2) $300
   (3) $900
   (4) $1,080
   (5) $3,000

7. A waist-to-hip ratio of greater than 0.8 has been identified as a predictor of early death for women. Which of the following is true?

   (1) A 24" waist and 34" hips would place a woman in a risky category.
   (2) A 200 pound woman would have to have a ratio bigger than 0.8.
   (3) A woman with a less than 0.8 ratio would have hips larger than her waist.
   (4) A woman with a less than 0.8 ratio would have hips smaller than her waist.
   (5) A teenager could not have a ratio less than 0.8.

8. The standard aspirin dose for a 150 pound adult is 650 milligrams. To calculate the number of milligrams that would be appropriate for a 60 pound child, which of these proportions would be correct?

   (1) $\dfrac{150}{650} = \dfrac{60}{x}$
   (2) $\dfrac{150}{650} = \dfrac{x}{60}$
   (3) $\dfrac{150}{60} = \dfrac{x}{650}$
   (4) $\dfrac{x}{150} = \dfrac{650}{60}$
   (5) $\dfrac{150}{x} = \dfrac{60}{650}$

9. Some stores pay their employees what is called a "graduated commission." Suppose your commission is 3% on all sales up to $8,000 and 5% on all sales above $8,000. What would be your commission if your sales for the month amounted to $15,000?

   (1) $590
   (2) $750
   (3) $4,066
   (4) $5,900
   (5) $7,450

10. Which is a factorization of $6a^2 - 7a - 24$?

    (1) $(3a - 4)(2a + 6)$
    (2) $(3a + 4)(2a - 6)$
    (3) $(3a + 8)(2a - 3)$
    (4) $(3a - 8)(2a + 3)$
    (5) $(6a + 12)(a - 2)$

11. Jan's computer is 133 megahertz, or 133,000,000 hertz. Express the last number in scientific notation.

    (1) 1.33×10^8
    (2) 1.33×10^{-8}
    (3) 13.3×10^{-8}
    (4) 13.3×10^8
    (5) 133×10^{-8}

12. Rhonda wants to estimate how much she could save yearly by using coupons. Her yearly grocery bill is about $5,000. On a typical trip to the store, she spends $100 and uses $8 in coupons. Which equation will allow her to predict her yearly savings from coupons?

 (1) $\dfrac{x}{5,000} = \dfrac{8}{100}$

 (2) $\dfrac{x}{8} = \dfrac{100}{5,000}$

 (3) $\dfrac{x}{100} = \dfrac{8}{5,000}$

 (4) $\dfrac{100}{5,000} = \dfrac{x}{8}$

 (5) Not enough information is given.

13. Find the value of x for $x = 3a(b - 2c)$ if $a = 5$, $b = 16$, and $c = 3$.

 (1) 150
 (2) 165
 (3) 195
 (4) 215
 (5) 240

14. In mapping an undersea trench off the coast of South America, the geologist begins at a depth of 200 feet. From there the probe falls 50 feet, then rises 30 feet, then drops again 100 feet. How many feet under the ocean's surface is the probe?

 (1) 80
 (2) –120
 (3) –280
 (4) –320
 (5) –380

15. Observe the order of operations to solve $48 \div (2 + 6) \times 2 - 1$.

 (1) 2
 (2) 8
 (3) 11
 (4) 36
 (5) 59

16. Which of the following inequalities describes the graph?

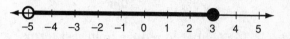

 (1) $-5 < x < 3$
 (2) $-5 < x < -3$
 (3) $-5 < x \le 3$
 (4) $-5 < x < 3$
 (5) $-5 < x$

ANSWERS

1. **3** Since every term in the expression $4a - 6a - 3a + a$ has the variable a, you can use the idea suggested in the signed number section of the chapter, in which you imagine that you are moving on a number line. You begin at the +4 position on the line, corresponding to the term $4a$. The next term is $-6a$, so you move 6 spaces to the left, putting you at –2. From this position you move 3 more spaces to the left because the next term is $-3a$. This move puts you at the –5 position on the number line. The last term in the problem is a, which is the same as $+1a$, so move 1 space in the positive direction. Your final position on the number line is therefore –4.

2. **1** The negative sign in the exponent tells you to move the decimal to the left because that is always the negative direction. The number 5 in the exponent means to move the decimal 5 spaces. Moving the decimal point in 3.4 to the left 5 spaces gives 0.000034.

3. **1** Whenever you see a problem that is set up in this manner, think of the cross multiply process. It does not matter which diagonal you begin with. One diagonal, containing the 4 and the 9, gives 36. The other diagonal, containing the 12 and the x, gives $12x$. Setting these equal to each other gives $12x = 36$. Dividing both sides by 12 gives $x = 3$.

4. **3** You can reason that if the teacher gets m dollars for 10 paychecks, then the total pay for the year is $10m$. Now

take that yearly income and split it into 12 pieces. The result is $10m$ divided by 12, or $\dfrac{10m}{12}$.

Remember to reduce to lowest terms, which gives $\dfrac{10m}{12} = \dfrac{5m}{6}$.

5. **1** Remember that when you are solving for a variable, you want to get the variable on one side by itself. There is more than one set of steps to work this problem, so if your steps vary from those shown here, do not be concerned unless you get the wrong answer.

$$3x + 8 = -12 + x$$
$$\underline{\quad -8 \quad\; -8 \quad\quad}$$ Subtract 8 from
$$3x = -20 + x \quad \text{both sides.}$$

$$3x = -20 + x$$
$$\underline{-x \qquad\; -x \quad}$$ Subtract x from
$$2x = -20 \qquad \text{both sides.}$$
$$x = -10 \qquad\;\; \text{Divide both sides by 2.}$$

6. **4** Remember the basic percent equation:

$$\text{Percent} = \frac{\text{part} \times 100}{\text{whole}}$$

Now substitute the numbers you know in the equation.

$$6 = \frac{\text{part} \times 100}{18,000}$$
$$(6)(18,000) = (\text{part})(100) \quad \text{Multiply both sides by 18,000.}$$
$$108,000 = (\text{part})(100)$$
$$1,080 = \text{part} \qquad \text{Divide both sides by 100.}$$

7. **3** The key idea in a ratio is to decide what to put on top and what on bottom. When reading a ratio, the first item mentioned goes on top and the second on the bottom. Therefore, when you read the phrase "waist-to-hip ratio," the waist size goes on top and the hip size on the bottom. In this and any ratio, if the bottom is bigger than the top, then the ratio will have a value less than 1. Since the value given for the ratio, 0.8, is less than 1, this means that the bottom of the ratio is bigger than the top. In

terms of what the body looks like, the hips are bigger than the waist, which is what choice 3 states.

8. **1** When you write a proportion, you must be consistent in positioning the values. Although there is more than one correct way to set up the proportion, the final answer will be the same. In the proportion that is the correct choice, notice that the first fraction is only about the adult and the second fraction is all about the child. Also, the numerators of both fractions give body weight and the denominators give milligrams of aspirin.

9. **1** The sales of $15,000 must be broken into two parts. These parts are the first $8,000 and the remainder, which is $7,000. To calculate the commission on the first $8,000 multiply it by 0.03 (which is 3%). This gives you $240. On the remainder (the $7,000), multiply by 0.05 (which is 5%) to get $350. The entire commission is the sum of $240 and $350, or $590.

10. **4** To determine which factorization is correct, multiply each set of possible factors using the FOIL technique. All of the choices give the correct answer for the product of the first terms and the last terms. Only choice 4, however, gives a sum of $-7a$ for the products of the outer and inner terms.

11. **1** When changing into scientific notation, the decimal must go between the first two digits. This will give the number 1.33 times 10 to some power. To decide on the power, count spaces from the new location of the decimal to the end of the number. This gives you 8 spaces. The only remaining part is to decide if the 8 is positive or negative. The sign will have to be positive. The reason for this is that you are moving the decimal in the positive direction when going from where the decimal is now to where the decimal was in the original problem.

12. **1** You might want to look back at Question 8 for another example of a

proportion. In this problem, you can let the first fraction be about the yearly grocery bill and the second be about the typical trip to the store. Within each fraction, let the numerator be the coupon savings and the denominator be the whole price of the purchases.

13. **1** The first step in a substitution problem is to write the equation itself. Then, directly below each letter, write the number value for that letter.

$x = 3\,a\,(\,b\,-2\,c)$
$x = 3(5)(16 - 2(3))$

Simplify using the order of operations.

$x = 3(5)(16 - 6)$
$x = 3(5)(10)$
$x = (15)(10)$
$x = 150$

14. **4** This is a number line problem with the number line vertical rather than horizontal. Imagine the probe starting at 200 feet under the water. The probe goes 50 feet farther down, leaving it 250 feet under the water. The probe then rises 30 feet, making the new depth 220 feet. The 100 foot drop puts the probe 320 feet below the surface. Depths below the surface of the water register as negative numbers, so the answer is –320.

15. **3** As you recall (or look back in the chapter to) order of operations, you will see that you should deal with the contents of the parentheses first, giving you 48 ÷ by 8 × 2 – 1. Next, do all of the multiplications and divisions in order. Dividing 48 by 8 gives 6. Multiplying 6 by 2 gives 12. Finally, subtracting 1 from 12 gives 11.

16. **3** The open circle at –5 tells you that –5 itself is not included. The closed circle at +3 tells you that +3 itself is included. The heavy line runs between these two numbers. Remember to put the equals part of the symbol with the +3 to show that the +3 is included.

Measurement

Measurement is one of the most frequently used math skills. Measurement is the key to everyday activities such as reading a speedometer, using a recipe, calculating your pay, and making home improvements. Measuring requires the use of a measuring device, whether it be a tape measure, a thermometer, a measuring cup, and so on. The first step in making measurements is to make certain that you understand the tool that you are using for making these measurements.

For example, look at the ruler shown below. The way to find out what each of the unmarked lines represents is to start by finding the halfway point between any two of the numbers. If you look at the ruler between 3 and 4, you can spot the halfway point. This tells you how many of the smallest spaces make a half inch. Count them to see that there are 8 spaces. Once you have figured out where ½ inch is on the ruler, ask yourself what would be half of a half. Because $\frac{1}{2} \times \frac{1}{2} = \frac{1}{4}$, you know where $\frac{1}{4}$ of an inch is and you can see that it takes 4 spaces to make $\frac{1}{4}$ of an inch. This same process will work for any measuring device.

PRACTICE

1. On a sketch of the ruler shown below,

   place a letter "A" at 1¾.
   place a letter "B" at 3⅝.
   place a letter "C" at ³⁄₁₆.
   place a letter "D at 2⅞.

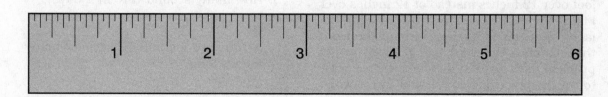

2. Use the barometer shown below to answer the following questions:

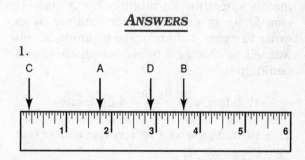

a. How much is each of the smallest spaces worth?

b. What is the reading at the arrow?

c. Place a mark where a reading of 29.8 inches would be.

d. Where would a reading of 31.2 inches be?

ANSWERS

1.

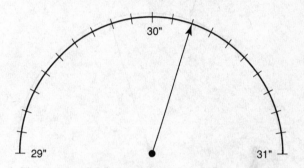

2a. **Each of the smallest spaces is equal to 0.1 inch. As you look at the distance between 30" and 31", you will see that there are 10 spaces. When you divide the 1" by 10, you get $\frac{1}{10}$, or 0.1.**

2b. **30.2"**

2c.

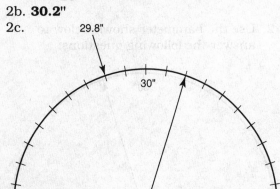

2d. **The value of 31.2" would be just off the right side of the scale.**

Conversion Factors

As you learn to analyze measuring devices and then to use measurements to solve problems, you will gain command of the GED topic called measurement. The problem solving part of measurement involves something called a *conversion factor*.

Conversion means change, and factor means something to multiply by. A conversion factor is something you multiply by in order to cause a change. For example, if you wanted to change 2.5 feet into inches, you could do this:

$$2.5 \text{ feet} \times \frac{12 \text{ inches}}{1 \text{ foot}} = 30 \text{ inches}$$

The 12 inches over 1 foot is the conversion factor.

You might wonder how we knew to write 1 foot over 12 inches instead of 12 inches over 1 foot. The decision is made by choosing the factor that has in its denominator the word that matches the word that is given in the problem itself, or that matches the numerator of the preceding conversion factor when more than one is used. This is so that the words will cancel out.

EXAMPLE

How many hours are there in 2 years?

Start out with the number that is in the problem:

$$2 \text{ years} \times \frac{356 \text{ days}}{1 \text{ year}} \times \frac{24 \text{ hours}}{1 \text{ day}} = \frac{17,520}{\text{hours}}$$

Because the years cancel and the days cancel, the answer is in hours.

Notice that in a conversion factor, the top and the bottom are always equal to each other. That is, you can use a conversion factor of 12 inches over 1 foot, but not one that says 6 inches over 1 foot because 6 inches and 1 foot are not equal.

The beauty of the conversion factor approach is that it tells you when to multiply and when to divide. Multiply by any number that appears in the numerator and divide by any number that appears in the denominator.

EXAMPLE

How many yards are in 144 inches?

$$144 \text{ inches} \times \frac{1 \text{ yard}}{36 \text{ inches}} = \frac{144}{36} = 4 \text{ yards}$$

Notice that the 36 is in the denominator, so you divide 36 into 144 to get 4. Also notice that the word inches in the denominator cancels the word inches in the numerator. The word that is not canceled will always give the units of the answer.

PRACTICE

3. How many weeks are in 105 days?

4. How many feet will equal 200 yards?

5. How many seconds are in 2 days?

6. A 100 yard football field is how many inches long?

ANSWERS

3. **105 days** $\times \dfrac{\textbf{1 week}}{\textbf{7 days}}$ = **15 weeks**

4. **200 yards** $\times \dfrac{\textbf{3 feet}}{\textbf{1 yard}}$ = **600 feet**

5. **2 days** $\times \dfrac{\textbf{24 hours}}{\textbf{1 day}} \times \dfrac{\textbf{60 minutes}}{\textbf{1 hour}} \times$
   $\dfrac{\textbf{60 seconds}}{\textbf{1 minute}}$ = **172,800 seconds**

6. **100 yards** $\times \dfrac{\textbf{36 inches}}{\textbf{1 yard}}$ = **3,600 inches**

Measurement of Time

Common Units of Time

60 seconds = 1 minute
60 minutes = 1 hour
24 hours = 1 day
7 days = 1 week
52 weeks = 1 year
365 days = 1 year

Time is a factor that you need to consider in nearly every phase of your life. As they say, "time is money," and certainly it is an economic factor. In measuring time, it is important that all of your numbers be in the same units when you are performing an operation. For example, you cannot multiply 1 hour and 10 minutes by 2 without considering that you have to have the hours and minutes in the same units, or multiply each separately. You can double the 1 hour and double the 10 minutes and get 2 hours and 20 minutes. This process runs into difficulty sometimes, however. What can you do to resolve the difficulty in doubling 2 hours and 45 minutes? You could double the 2 hours and get 4 hours, but when you double 45 minutes, you get 90 minutes. It would not be good form to write the answer as 4 hours and 90 minutes, so you would have to think of 90 minutes as 1 hour and 30 minutes. Adding this to the 4 hours would revise your

result to a total of 5 hours and 30 minutes. Fortunately, common sense can always help you with time manipulations.

PRACTICE

7. Calculate the time Sally will be paid for this week if she works the following hours:

   Monday: 4 hours and 15 minutes

   Tuesday: 5 hours and 40 minutes

   Wednesday: 3 hours and 20 minutes

   Thursday: off

   Friday: 4 hours and 5 minutes

8. Calculate the number of minutes in one week.

9. If your daily commuting time is one hour and thirty-five minutes, how much time does commuting take for a five day workweek?

ANSWERS

7. **The total time is 16 hours plus 80 minutes, or 17 hours and 20 minutes.**

8. **1 week** $\times \dfrac{\textbf{7 days}}{\textbf{1 week}} \times \dfrac{\textbf{24 hours}}{\textbf{1 day}} \times$
   $\dfrac{\textbf{60 minutes}}{\textbf{1 hour}}$ = **10,080 minutes**

9. **5(1 hour and 35 minutes) = 5 hours and 175 minutes. To convert 175 minutes to hours, think of 2 hours as 120 minutes, which leaves 55 minutes. Then 5 hours plus 2 hours and 55 minutes equals 7 hours and 55 minutes.**

Weight Measurement

Common Units of Weight
16 ounces = 1 pound
1,000 mg = 1 gram
2,000 pounds = 1 ton

Weight is a topic of interest for groceries, home improvement projects, recipes—even for workouts at the fitness center. The most common units of weight are the pound and the ounce. Medicinal weights are often given in milligrams and grams.

When working with weight problems, it is necessary that you make all of the units the same, so that you can compare better. For example, suppose that in shopping for laundry detergent you wanted to compare these two boxes:

Brand A   5 pounds 10 ounces
Brand B   100 ounces

To convert Brand A into ounces, use the approach of conversion factors.

$$5 \text{ pounds} \times \frac{16 \text{ ounces}}{1 \text{ pound}} + 10 \text{ ounces} =$$
90 ounces

Now it will be easier to see the relationship between Box A at 90 ounces and Box B at 100 ounces.

PRACTICE

10. What will Joan's total amount of hamburger be if she bought the packages listed below?

   #1: 3 lbs 8 ounces
   #2: 2 lbs 9 ounces
   #3: 4 lbs 2 ounces

11. An elevator has a sign stating that it has a one ton capacity. How many people would this be if the average person weighs 200 pounds?

12. Prices for livestock are often given by the "hundred weight," that is, by the price for 100 pounds. What would be the price of a 750 pound cow if it were listed at $90.00 for a hundred weight?

ANSWERS

10. **Add the pounds to get 9 lbs. When you add the ounces, you get 19 ounces. Recalling that there are 16 ounces in a pound, the 19 ounces is equal to 1 pound and 3 ounces. Add this to the 9 pounds, and the total weight is 10 pounds and 3 ounces.**
11. **One ton is 2000 pounds. Divide this by 200 pounds to get 10 persons.**
12. **A 750 pound cow is 7.5 hundred weight $\left(\dfrac{750}{100} = 7.5 \right)$. If the cost is $90 per hundred weight, you multiply the 90 by 7.5, getting $675.**

Liquid Measurement

Common Units of Liquid Measure
2 cups = 1 pint
2 pints = 1 quart
4 quarts = 1 gallon

The measurement of liquids includes pumping gasoline, buying soft drinks, and mixing fuel for lawn equipment.

EXAMPLE

How many quarts of antifreeze are equal to 2.5 gallons?

$$2.5 \text{ gallons} \times \frac{4 \text{ quarts}}{1 \text{ gallon}} = 10 \text{ quarts}$$

Notice that the gallons cancel each other, leaving only quarts. You always want the word that does not cancel to be the units for the answer.

PRACTICE

13. How many cups are in 10 quarts?

14. How many quarts are in 10 cups?

15. How many pints are there in 3 gallons?

16. How many quarts of orange juice would you need to buy in order to have 30 gallons for the town pancake breakfast?

17. A case of motor oil contains 12 quarts. How many gallons is this?

ANSWERS

13. **10 quarts** $\times \dfrac{\textbf{4 cups}}{\textbf{1 quart}} = \textbf{40 cups}$

14. **10 cups** $\times \dfrac{\textbf{1 quart}}{\textbf{4 cups}} = \textbf{2.5 quarts}$

15. **3 gallons** $\times \dfrac{\textbf{4 quarts}}{\textbf{1 gallon}} \times \dfrac{\textbf{2 pints}}{\textbf{1 quart}} =$ **24 pints**

16. **30 gallons** $\times \dfrac{\textbf{4 quarts}}{\textbf{1 gallon}} = \textbf{120 quarts}$

17. **12 quarts** $\times \dfrac{\textbf{1 gallon}}{\textbf{4 quarts}} = \textbf{3 gallons}$

Dry Measure

Common Units of Dry Measure
3 teaspoons = 1 tablespoon
4 tablespoons = $\frac{1}{4}$ cup
2 pints = 1 quart
8 quarts = 1 peck
4 pecks = 1 bushel

Dry measure is a way to measure volume rather than weight. For example, a quart of blackberries tells you what size container will be filled with berries, but makes no claim about what those berries will weigh. Dry measure is a convenient way to measure things whose weight may vary. Berries, nuts, cereal, rice, and pasta are things that are often measured with the units shown above.

PRACTICE

18. If you were preparing a recipe but you could not find your measuring cup, how many tablespoons would you use to get $\frac{3}{4}$ cup of sugar?

19. One market sells peaches by the peck and another market sells by the bushel. If peaches are selling for $6.50 for a bushel, how much will those peaches cost by the peck?

ANSWERS

18. $\dfrac{3}{4}$ **cup** $\times \dfrac{\textbf{4 tablespoons}}{\frac{1}{4}\textbf{ cup}} =$ **12 tablespoons**

19. $\dfrac{\textbf{\$6.50}}{\textbf{1 bushel}} \times \dfrac{\textbf{1 bushel}}{\textbf{4 pecks}} = \textbf{\$1.63/peck}$

Metric Measure

The metric system is based on prefixes whose meanings tell you about their size. The most common of these prefixes follow:

milli = one thousandth
centi = one hundredth
deca = one tenth
kilo = one thousand
mega = one million (10^6)
giga = one billion (10^9)

There are also common units. Grams are used for weight, meters for length, and liters for volume. Combining the common units with the prefixes allows you to find the sizes of various metric measurements.

For example, using the system above, you can see that a kilogram is 1,000 grams, since kilo means 1,000. Centimeter means one hundredth of a meter, or 0.01 meter.

Common Units of Metric Measure
1 centimeter = 10 millimeters
1 meter = 100 centimeters
1 kilometer = 1,000 meters
1 milligram = 0.001 grams
1 kilogram = 1,000 grams
1 liter = 1,000 milliliters

The idea of *metric* scares many people. However, after they have worked with metric measures for awhile, they begin to see that it is really the easiest system of all. What makes it so easy is that moving around in the metric system is just a matter of moving the decimal point.

EXAMPLE

How many millimeters (mm) equal 55 centimeters (cm)?

$$55 \text{ cm} \times \frac{10 \text{ mm}}{1 \text{ cm}} = 550 \text{ mm}$$

The reason that you know to use the conversion factor with centimeters in the denominator is that you want to be able to cancel the centimeters in 55 centimeters. The word left after the cancellation gives the units of the answer.

20. How many times more bytes does a gigabyte computer have than a megabyte computer?

21. How many grams of aspirin are in a 325 milligram pill?

22. How many meters are equal to a 2.5 kilometer run?

ANSWERS

20. **1,000; Mega means 1 million, and giga means 1 billion, which is 1,000 million.**

21. $\textbf{325 milligrams} \times \dfrac{\textbf{1 gram}}{\textbf{1,000 milligrams}} =$ **0.325 gram**

22. $\textbf{2.5 kilometer} \times \dfrac{\textbf{1,000 meters}}{\textbf{1 kilometer}} =$ **2,500 meters**

End of Chapter Practice

As you work your way through these measurement practice questions, remember that you are free to use the tables that are within the chapter that give the common units for measurements. These will also be available on the GED exam.

1. The distance between the two marks on the dipstick shown below is 1 quart. If you only had access to a kitchen measuring cup, how many cupfuls would be needed to take the oil level from the add mark to the full mark.

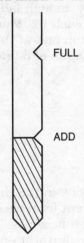

   (1) 1
   (2) 2
   (3) 4
   (4) 6
   (5) 8

2. In a scene from an adventure film, the hero is shown grabbing up a sack filled with gold. The hero runs with the gold as if it were not hard to carry. How much does the gold weigh if gold weighs 19 grams per milliliter and the sack is a 2 liter sack?

   (1) $19 \times 2 \times 1,000$

   (2) $\dfrac{19}{2 \times 1,000}$

   (3) $\dfrac{2 \times 1,000}{19}$

   (4) $\dfrac{19 \times 2}{1,000}$

   (5) Not enough information is given.

3. About how long do you need to bake a roast if it requires 28 minutes per pound and the roast weighs 5.3 pounds?

   (1) 1 hour 48 minutes
   (2) 2 hours 28 minutes
   (3) 2 hours 47 minutes
   (4) 2 hours 54 minutes
   (5) Not enough information is given.

4. The following represents a time card, which records your times of arrival and departure at work for one day. What were your total hours of work for the day?

   In: 8:50
   Out: 11:45
   In: 12:30
   Out: 5:35

   (1) 8 hours
   (2) 8 hours 15 minutes
   (3) 8 hours 35 minutes
   (4) 8 hours 45 minutes
   (5) 9 hours 54 minutes

5. The owner's manual for your car states that your gas tank holds 15 gallons of gas. If the gauge looks like the one shown below, approximately how many gallons will be in the tank?

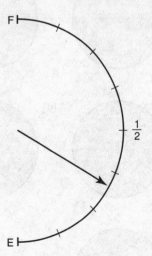

   (1) 2 gallons
   (2) 3 gallons
   (3) 5 gallons
   (4) 6 gallons
   (5) 7 gallons

6. The recipe calls for $\frac{3}{4}$ cup of ketchup and $\frac{1}{4}$ cup of vinegar. If you have only $\frac{1}{2}$ cup of ketchup, how many cups of vinegar should you use?

   (1) $\frac{1}{8}$

   (2) $\frac{1}{6}$

   (3) $\frac{1}{5}$

   (4) $\frac{1}{4}$

   (5) $\frac{1}{3}$

7. A prescription medication for flea control in dogs calls for a tablet that is 204 milligrams for a 50 pound dog. Which of the ways of equally dividing the tablet shown below would be closest to the right dosage for a 10 pound dog?

(1) 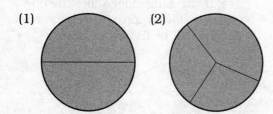 (2)

(3) 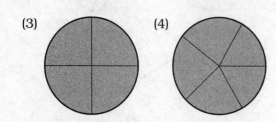 (4)

(5)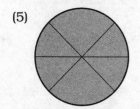

8. A catalog offers 950 milliliters of Diet Nectar for sale. In another catalog there is an ad for Diet Nectar, but it is given in liters. Which of the following shows how many liters would be comparable to the amount in first catalog?

   (1) 0.0950
   (2) 0.950
   (3) 9.50
   (4) 95.0
   (5) 950.0

9. Rita has selected drapery fabric whose width is perfect for her windows. She needs to buy enough fabric to make two panels, each 62" long with a 5" hem at the top and at the bottom. How many yards of fabric should she buy?

   (1) 2
   (2) 4
   (3) 6
   (4) 12
   (5) 72

10. Each time zone in the United States is 1 hour different from each of its neighboring time zones. The most eastern zone (farthest on the right) is the latest of the zones shown on the map. When it is 8 P.M. in city A, what time is it in city B?

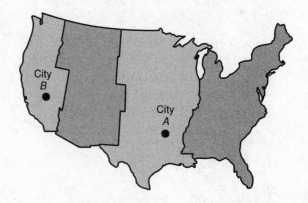

   (1) 6 P.M.
   (2) 7 P.M.
   (3) 8 P.M.
   (4) 9 P.M.
   (5) 10 P.M.

11. The label on a quart milk carton states that it contains 946 milliliters of milk. How many liters is this?

    (1) 0.00946
    (2) 0.0946
    (3) 0.946
    (4) 94,600
    (5) 946,000

12. A bottle of vitamin C crystals states that there are 250 grams of crystals in the bottle and that 1 teaspoon equals 5,000 milligrams. How many teaspoonfuls are in the bottle?

    (1) 10
    (2) 20
    (3) 50
    (4) 100
    (5) 200

13. A 1 pound box of chocolates contains 32 pieces of candy. How many calories are in each piece of candy if 1 ounce of candy has 100 calories?

    (1) 20
    (2) 25
    (3) 50
    (4) 75
    (5) 100

14. An airplane flies at 30,000 feet. How many miles is this if there are 5,280 feet in one mile?

    (1) (30,000)(5,280)
    (2) $\dfrac{30,000}{5,280}$
    (3) $\dfrac{5,280}{30,000}$
    (4) 30,000 × 1,760
    (5) $\dfrac{30,000}{1,760}$

15. If gasoline prices go up 4 cents on the gallon, how much will that cost you yearly if you buy an average of 15 gallons of gasoline each week?

    (1) $13.87
    (2) $31.20
    (3) $312.00
    (4) $138.67
    (5) $3,120.00

16. Stan reads the labels on pain killers:

    Regular strength:
        100 pills $5.00   325 mg

    Extra strength:
        100 pills $10.00   500 mg

    Which of these can you conclude from these labels?

    (1) Regular strength is the best buy.
    (2) Extra strength is the best buy.
    (3) They are the same value.
    (4) They cannot be compared.
    (5) Not enough information is given.

17. In designing the can for pineapple slices, the dimensions shown below have been taken into consideration. Pineapple slices are stacked, one on top of the other, in the can. How many slices will fit in the can?

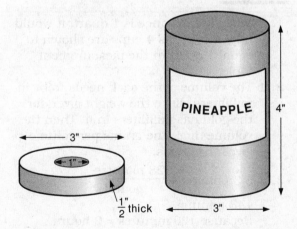

    (1) 6
    (2) 8
    (3) 10
    (4) 12
    (5) 14

18. How many one quart containers would be needed to transport $2\frac{1}{2}$ gallons of gasoline?

    (1) 5
    (2) 7.5
    (3) 10
    (4) 15
    (5) 20

19. A peanut butter label states the following:

    2 tablespoons = 1 serving size
    90 calories per serving

    If your typical peanut butter sandwich has 2 teaspoons of peanut butter, how many calories of peanut butter is that?

    (1) 30
    (2) 60
    (3) 90
    (4) 120
    (5) 180

ANSWERS

1. **3** Since the distance is 1 quart, it would take 4 cups, as 4 cups are shown to equal 1 quart in the measurement table.

2. **1** The volume of the sack needs to be in milliliters, since the weight given for the gold has milliliters in it. Then the volume times the grams per volume gives the grams.

3. **2** $5.3 \text{ pounds} \times \dfrac{28 \text{ minutes}}{1 \text{ pound}} =$
   148 minutes
   Because 120 minutes = 2 hours, 148 minutes equals 2 hours with 28 minutes left over.

4. **1** Working from 8:50 to 11:45 gives 2 hours 55 minutes, and working from 12:30 to 5:35 gives 5 hours

5 minutes, so the totoal is 7 hours 60 minutes, or 8 hours.

5. **3** There are 4 divisions in $\frac{1}{2}$ tank, so each mark represents $\frac{1}{8}$ tank. The amount is a little less than $\frac{3}{8}$ of 15, or about 5 gallons.

6. **2** You can use a proportion approach:
   $$\frac{\frac{3}{4} \text{ cup ketchup}}{\frac{1}{4} \text{ cup vinegar}} = \frac{\frac{1}{2} \text{ cup ketchup}}{x \text{ cups vinegar}}$$

7. **4** Since 10 is $\frac{1}{5}$ of 50, the whole pill would need to be split into five parts.

8. **2** $950 \text{ milliliters} \times \dfrac{1 \text{ liter}}{1,000 \text{ milliliters}} =$
   0.950 liters

9. **2** Each panel will need to be 72 inches long (the 62 inches of the drape plus 10 inches for the top and bottom hems). For two panels, that will mean 144 inches of fabric.
   $$144 \text{ inches} \times \frac{1 \text{ yard}}{36 \text{ inches}} = 4 \text{ yards}$$

10. **1** The time zone for city B is 2 zones (hours) earlier than city A.

11. **3** $946 \text{ milliliters} \times \dfrac{1 \text{ liter}}{1,000 \text{ milliliters}} =$
    0.946 liters

12. **3** $250 \text{ grams} \times \dfrac{1,000 \text{ milligrams}}{1 \text{ gram}} \times$
    $\dfrac{1 \text{ teaspoon}}{5,000 \text{ mg}} = 50 \text{ teaspoons}$

13. **3** $\dfrac{1 \text{ box}}{32 \text{ pieces}} \times \dfrac{1 \text{ pound}}{1 \text{ box}} \times \dfrac{16 \text{ ounces}}{1 \text{ pound}} \times$
    $\dfrac{100 \text{ calories}}{1 \text{ ounce}} = 50 \text{ calories/piece}$

14. **2** $30,000 \text{ feet} \times \dfrac{1 \text{ mile}}{5,280 \text{ feet}}$

15. **2** $\dfrac{\$0.04}{1 \text{ gallon}} \times \dfrac{15 \text{ gallons}}{1 \text{ week}} \times \dfrac{52 \text{ weeks}}{1 \text{ year}} =$
    $31.20/year

16. **1** You would have to pay twice as much for extra strength, but you would not get twice the milligrams. Since extra strength has no extra ingredients, just more of the painkiller, it is not as good a buy.

17. **2** Everything is information that you do not need except for two things—the thickness of the pineapple slice and the height of the can. You can fit 8 one-half inch slices into a four inch can.

18. **3** 2.5 gallons $\times \dfrac{4 \text{ quarts}}{1 \text{ gallon}} = 10$ quarts

19. **1** 2 teaspoons $\times \dfrac{1 \text{ tablespoon}}{3 \text{ teaspoons}} \times$

$\dfrac{90 \text{ calories}}{2 \text{ tablespoons}} = 30$ calories

Geometry

Geometry makes all the difference. As you look at the world with an eye to shape, size, and angles, you will become increasingly aware of the role of geometry. On the GED mathematics test, approximately 20% of the questions will have a basis in geometry. The good news is that the test does not assume that you have done well in geometry in school, but rather that you can read about a situation, study a diagram about that situation, and come to correct conclusions. The focus of the GED test is to see how well you can deal with everyday life situations that you will find at home, in the marketplace, and on the job.

There are geometry ideas that are not covered in this chapter because they are not required by the GED test. The geometry ideas that you will need to be able to handle for the GED are the following:

- lines and angles
- shapes, including rectangles, squares, triangles, circles, cubes, rectangular solids, and cylinders
- perimeter, area, and volume

Lines and Angles

Everywhere you look, you see lines and angles. Lines define boundaries, mark highways, create pictures, form logos, make designs. Lines form angles in the corner of a room, the slope of the road, the direction the halfback runs with the ball.

LINES

The vocabulary of lines includes "horizontal," "vertical," and "parallel." If any of these words are unfamiliar to you, make index cards for them. The diagram below will help you to understand horizontal and vertical lines.

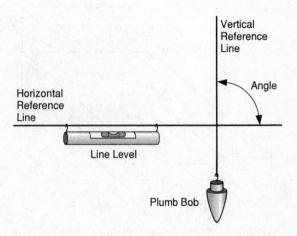

As you can see from the illustration above, a horizontal line is a line that runs across. You might remember it by relating it to the word "horizon," the line that is the boundary between Earth and sky. Since a vertical line runs up and down, you might link it in your mind to a basketball player's vertical leap.

Parallel lines are lines that are the same distance apart, no matter at which point they are measured. The yard markers on a football field are parallel lines. The 40-yard line is parallel to the 30-yard line; the 30-yard line is parallel to the goal line, and so on. It does not matter how far apart the lines are, as long as they would never meet, no matter how long they were extended.

In the rectangle below, the horizontal lines are parallel and the vertical lines are parallel. You will often see parallel lines designated this way:

$$AB \parallel CD$$
$$AC \parallel BD$$

PRACTICE

Suppose you were in charge of building an enclosure for the community tennis courts, as pictured below. Examine the diagram and to answer Questions 1–4.

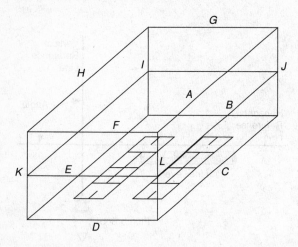

1. Which of the lettered lines are horizontal?

2. Which of the lettered lines are vertical?

3. Which of the lettered lines are parallel to line *B*?

4. Which of the lettered lines are parallel to line *F*?

5. Suppose that in giving directions, someone says that his home is on a road that runs parallel to the river. Which of the diagrams shown below reflects this statement?

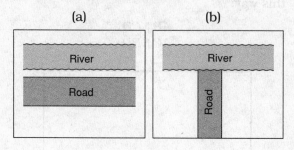

ANSWERS

1. ***A, B, C, D, E, F, G, H***
2. ***I, J, K, L***
3. ***A, C, H***
4. ***D, E, G***
5. **(a)**

ANGLES

Everywhere you look, angles come into view. Angles are formed where lines meet. The GED test will not ask you to name angles, or to measure them, but rather to evaluate them and their relationship to everyday objects and events.

ANGLES AND THEIR MEASURE

Remembering that there are 360° (360 degrees) in a circle will help you picture various angles. Notice in the figure below that the circle is split into four parts, *A, B, C* and *D*.

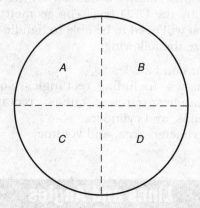

If you divide the 360° into four parts, you get four angles measuring 90° each.

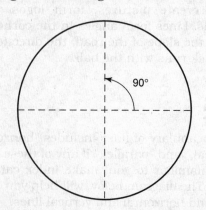

Once you can see a 90° angle in your mind, you can imagine a 45° angle by picturing half of the 90° angle.

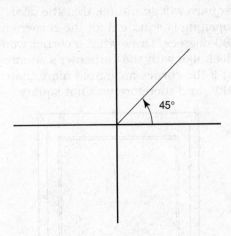

You can then picture a 30° angle and a 60° angle by imagining the 90° angle (also called a right angle) divided into thirds, as shown below.

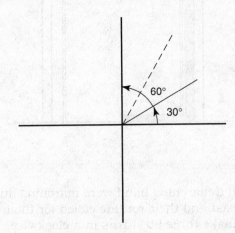

There is a special symbol, as shown below, to indicate a right angle.

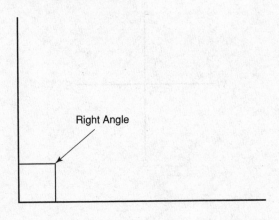

As you learn more geometry, try to visualize the concepts. Whenever you can, draw a diagram to help you picture each relationship.

PRACTICE

In each diagram below, there is an angle marked with an *x*. Find the number of degrees in each marked angle.

6.

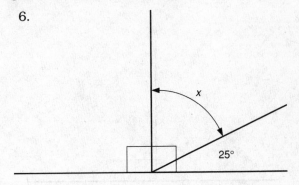

7.

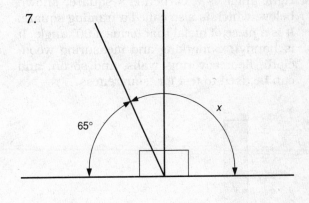

ANSWERS

6. **65°; 90° − 25° = 65°**
7. **115°; 90° + (90° − 65°) = 90° + 25° = 115°**

THE "SQUARE" ANGLE

There is a special angle, called a right angle or a square angle, that is especially important in the world around us. This angle shows up in constructing buildings, designing playing fields, making picture frames, and laying out street plans, to name just a few.

A right angle is one that measures 90°. The presence of the 90° angle makes the two lines that create the angle square to each other, or *perpendicular*. If two lines k and l are perpendicular to each other, as shown in the figure below, we indicate this by writing $k \perp l$.

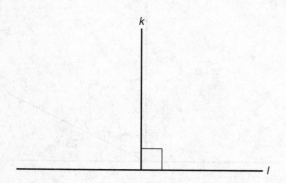

One of several tools you can use to produce a right angle is a carpenter's square, shown below, which is also called a framing square. It is a piece of metal that forms a 90° angle. It is handy for marking and measuring wood, cloth, floor covering, walls, and so on, and can be used to test for "squareness."

PRACTICE

8. In the diagram below, the carpenter's square will guarantee that the door opening is square if all the corners are 90 degrees. Draw what a corner would look like with the carpenter's square in it if the corner measured more than 90°, and therefore was not square.

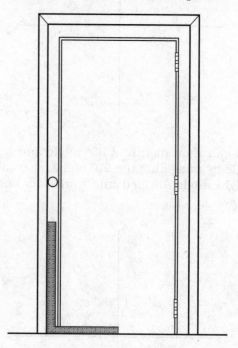

9. If a marching band were marching due east and their routine called for them to make three 90° turns in a clockwise direction, in which direction would they now be marching?

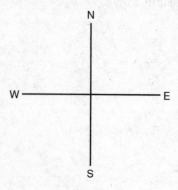

ANSWERS

8.

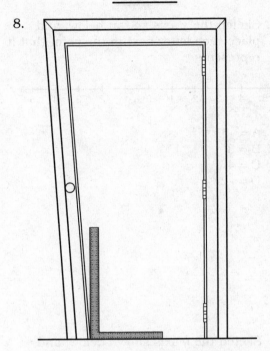

9. **north; The first turn would make them head south; the 2nd turn would make them head west; the 3rd turn would make them head north**

ANGLES AND PARALLEL LINES

If you were laying out a garden or a tennis court or some other space in which you wanted to have parallel lines, the idea illustrated below could help you.

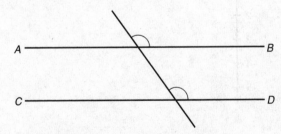

A ———————————————— B

C ———————————————— D

If you know that the angles marked with a ⌒ are equal to each other, then you know that line *AB* is parallel to line *CD*.

The same idea holds for other angle pairs formed by a line crossing two parallel lines. In the diagram below, you can be certain that

line $\overline{AB}$ is parallel to line $\overline{CD}$ if any of the relationships shown is true (the symbol ∠ indicates an angle).

$$\angle x = \angle y \quad \angle t = \angle u \quad \angle r = \angle s$$

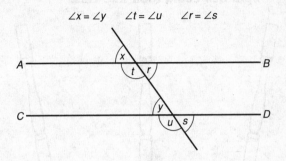

PRACTICE

10. Which strategy illustrated below would guarantee that the spindles of a deck railing are parallel?

(a)

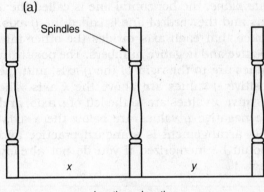

Spindles

length *x* = length *y*

(b)

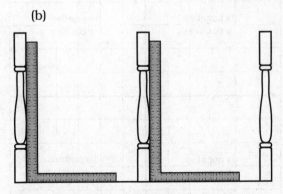

Use a carpenter square, which makes certain that the angles are 90°.

10. **(b); If you used choice (a), the spindles could look like this:**

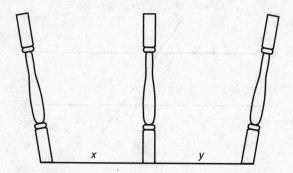

Coordinates

In the figure below, which shows the *coordinate plane*, the horizontal line is called the *x* axis and the vertical line is called the *y* axis. Notice that each axis divides the other into positive and negative numbers. The positive *x* values are to the right of the *y* axis, and the positive *y* values are above the *x* axis. The negative *x* values are to the left of *y* axis, and the negative *y* values are below the *x* axis. This arrangement is standard practice and should be memorized if you do not already know it.

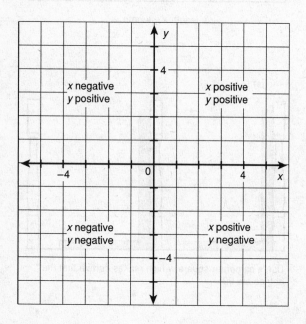

11. Sketch the *x* axis shown below, and place each letter next to the point that it represents.

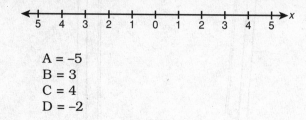

A = –5
B = 3
C = 4
D = –2

12. Sketch the *y* axis shown below, and place each letter next to the point that it represents.

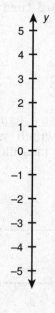

E = –2
F = 2
G = 0
H = –3

When working with the coordinate plane, it is also standard practice to use a pair of numbers in parentheses, separated by a comma, to designate values for *x* and *y*. The *x* is always given first, so if you see two numbers written in this manner, such as (–3, 5), this means that the first number gives the *x* coordinate, or the measurement along the *x* axis, and the second number gives the *y* coordinate, or the measurement along the *y* axis. To find the location for the point with coordinates (–3, 5) travel on the *x* axis 3 spaces to the left of zero (you go left because you are locating negative 3), and then travel up 5 spaces (you would have gone down if the 5 had been a negative 5). The location of (–3, 5) is shown on the coordinate plane below.

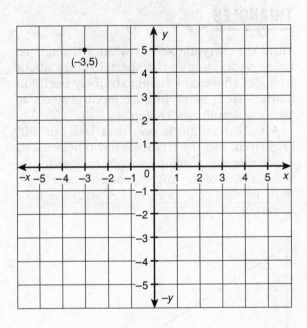

13. Give the coordinates in the form (*x*, *y*) for each of the points labeled on the coordinate plane below.

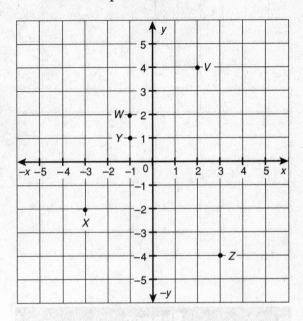

ANSWERS

11.

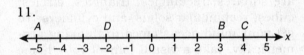

12.

13.

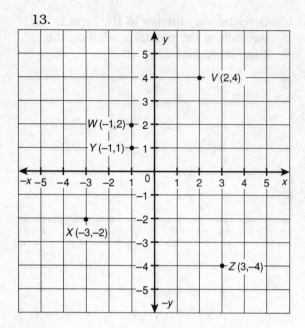

Shapes

Some of the shapes that dominate our world are squares, rectangles, triangles, circles, cubes, rectangular solids, and cylinders. To get your mind accustomed to thinking geometrically, take a visual tour of your home to see where these shapes are. As you do this, you will be laying the foundation for your analysis of GED questions. The people who make the GED test look for geometry ideas in the home, the marketplace, and the workplace when they write questions. Becoming more aware of the geometry all around you will help you be ready for these questions.

Squares

Squares have four sides that all have the same length. Every angle in a square is a right angle, or 90° angle.

Rectangles

Rectangles have four sides, all meeting at right angles. Each pair of opposite sides has the same length. No matter how a rectangle is turned, the longer sides measure the length, and the shorter sides measure the width.

Triangles

Triangles have three sides. The properties of triangles are so useful for GED topics that a detailed analysis of triangles follows.

Circles

Circles are collections of all the points that are the same distance, called the radius, from a given point, called the center.

Cylinders

Perhaps the most familiar cylinder is the soft drink can. A cylinder can be thought of as a stack of circles, as the circle defines many of the mathematical properties of cylinders.

TRIANGLES

Although everyone knows what a triangle is, not everyone knows the special things about triangles that make them extremely useful in matters from home improvement projects to laying out quilting designs.

A right triangle is one that has one 90° angle in it, like the triangle shown below. You can recognize a right triangle by looking to see that one of the angles looks like the angle that the wall of a room makes with the floor or ceiling.

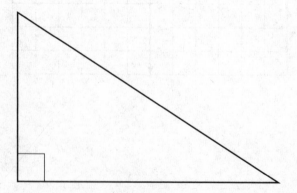

Some special right triangles that are very useful are shown below.

Notice that the total number of degrees in both the 45°, 45°, 90° triangle and the 30°, 60°, 90° triangle is 180°. It turns out that this is true not just for these triangles, but for *all* triangles. That is, the total number of degrees in the angles of a triangle is always 180.

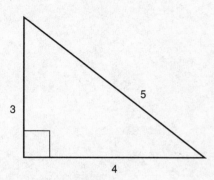

The 3, 4, 5 right triangle

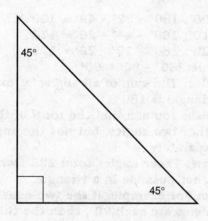

The 45°, 45°, 90° right triangle

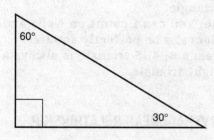

The 30°, 60°, 90° right triangle

PRACTICE

For each triangle below, calculate the number of degrees in the angle marked *x*:

14.

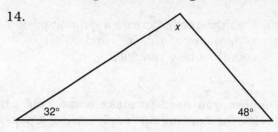

15.

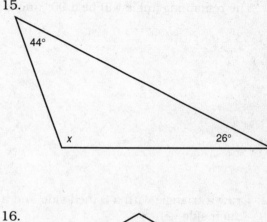

16.

Decide whether each of the following statements is true or false:

17. If two angles of a triangle add up to 90°, the third angle will have to be 90°.

18. The bigger the triangle is, the larger the sum of its angles.

19. If you know the number of degrees in one angle, you can find the other two angles.

20. If you wanted to create a quilting piece with angles of 45°, 90°, and 90°, it could not be a triangle.

Suppose you need to make some kind of device for drawing 90° angles using a pencil, a ruler, scissors, and cardboard. Decide whether each of the following will work:

21. Make a triangle with two equal angles. The remaining angle will be a 90° angle.

22. Draw a triangle with a 3 inch side and a 4 inch side.

23. Use a corner in one room of the house as a guide.

24. Draw a triangle with a 3 inch side and a 4 inch side, and adjust the triangle until the remaining side is 5 inches.

ANSWERS

14. **100°; 180° – 32° – 48° = 100°**
15. **110°; 180° – 44° – 26° = 110°**
16. **122°; 180° – 29° – 29° = 122°**
17. **true; 180° – 90° = 90°**
18. **false; The sum of all angles of *any* triangle is 180°.**
19. **false; You can find the *total* of the other two angles, but not the angles separately.**
20. **true; These angles total 225°, which is not possible in a triangle.**
21. **no; For example, if the two equal angles are each 20°, then the third angle equals 180° – 40° = 140°**
22. **no; a 3 inch side and a 4 inch side won't assure that the other side will be a 5 inch side, creating a right triangle.**
23. **no; You can't count on walls and floors to be perfectly square.**
24. **yes; a 3, 4, 5 triangle is always a right triangle.**

THE PYTHAGOREAN RELATIONSHIP

Pythagoras was an early mathematician who discovered something very useful about right triangles. He found that if you take a right triangle, such as the one below, the equation shown is always true:

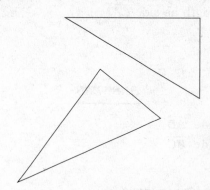

$$a^2 + b^2 = c^2$$

That is, if you square the lengths of each of the sides that form the right angle, and then add the squares, their sum equals the squares of the length of the side across from the right angle. The sides that form the 90° angle (a and b) are called the legs, and the side opposite the 90° angle (c) is called the hypotenuse. This special right triangle relationship is called the Pythagorean relationship.

PRACTICE

25. Use the Pythagorean relationship to find the length of the hypotenuse in the triangle below.

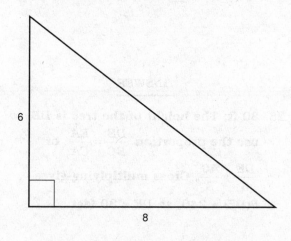

ANSWER

25. **10; $a^2 + b^2 = 6^2 + 8^2 = 36 + 64 = 100$, so $c^2 = 100$, which is true for $c = 10$.**

CONGRUENT TRIANGLES

Congruent is a fancy word that basically means the same size and shape. If you were trying to decide if two triangles are congruent, imagine that you cut out a pattern of one of the triangles. If you can turn that pattern to make it fit perfectly on top of the other triangle, the two triangles are congruent.

For example, the triangles below could be turned to fit each other perfectly, so they are congruent.

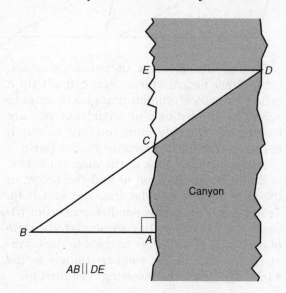

You might ask what good it is to know that triangles are congruent. The idea is most often used as a way to find distances or angles that you cannot measure directly. For example, if you wanted to know the distance between the two sides of the canyon in the diagram below, it would certainly be nice if you did not have to measure that distance directly. You can lay out a congruent triangle over the land that is easy to measure, so you can indirectly measure the canyon width.

$AB \parallel DE$

Use the preceding figure to answer Questions 26 and 27.

26. Which side in triangle *ABC* corresponds to the distance across the canyon?

27. For the two triangles to be congruent, which side would have to be the same length as side $\overline{CA}$?

ANSWERS

26. **side $\overline{AB}$**
27. **side $\overline{EC}$**

SIMILAR TRIANGLES

Two triangles are similar if you could take a picture of one triangle and either enlarge or shrink the picture to fit the second triangle. The triangle on the left below could be reduced to get the triangle on the right, so they are similar.

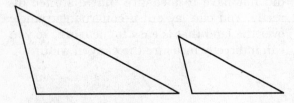

Similar triangles are useful, once again, for indirect measurement. You can set up a ratio between two similar triangles in order to solve for the distance or angle that you are looking for. The only thing you have to watch is that you really do compare similar parts.

As an example, look at the diagram below. It would be no easy job to find the height of the tree directly. Similar triangles can help. Triangle *ABC* is just a smaller version of triangle *ADE*. Because they are similar, the ratio of each side of the larger triangle to the corresponding side of the smaller triangle is the same. This gives the following relationship:

$$\frac{DE}{BC} = \frac{DA}{BA} = \frac{EA}{CA}$$

Notice also that the two triangles have the same angles.

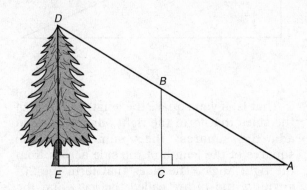

PRACTICE

28. Calculate the height of the tree shown above from these measurements:

EA = 40 feet
BC = 6 feet
CA = 8 feet

ANSWER

28. **30 ft; The height of the tree is *DE*, so use the proportion $\dfrac{DE}{BC} = \dfrac{EA}{CA}$, or**

$$\frac{DE}{6} = \frac{40}{8}.$$ **Cross multiplying gives**

8(*DE*) = 240, so *DE* = 30 feet.

CIRCLES

From automobile tires to cake pans, circles play a large part in our everyday lives. The parts of a circle are terms that you need to memorize if you do not already know them. These parts are the <u>circumference</u>, the <u>radius</u>, and the <u>diameter</u>, as shown below. If you have difficulty remembering any of these terms, make a note card for your study.

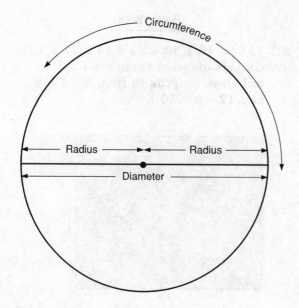

29. $2\frac{1}{2}$ **in.; The radius is half of the diameter.**

30. **24 corresponds to B, 18 to C, and 12 to A, since 24 gauge is the thinnest wire and 12 gauge is the thickest.**

CYLINDERS

This is a cylinder:

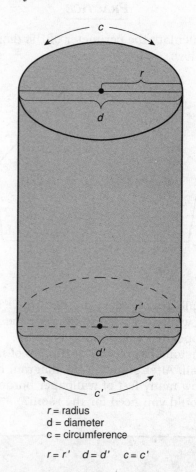

r = radius
d = diameter
c = circumference

r = r'   d = d'   c = c'

PRACTICE

29. Suppose that you want to install a radio speaker in the door of your automobile. The instructions say that you need a hole with a 5 inch diameter. If your drill attachment that makes circular holes is set for radius, what radius should you choose?

30. Wire is manufactured in sizes ranging from as thin as a thread to quite thick. The size is described by the word "gauge." Strangely enough, the fatter the wire, the smaller the gauge. Knowing this, match the different gauges to the letter of the wire to which it must correspond.

Gauge of Wire	Diameter of Wire
24	A: 13.1 mm
18	B: 5.2 mm
12	C: 7.0 mm

The top and bottom of cylinders are circles, so you can describe a cylinder using radius, diameter, and circumference. Familiar cylinders include soup cans, prescription bottles, and a roll of candy.

Since cylinders are usually containers, the volume of a cylinder is a frequent consideration. The topic of volume will be taken up later in the chapter.

Using Shapes

PERIMETER

If the word *perimeter* is not something that you already know, think about putting a fence around a field or lawn. The total length of the fence gives the perimeter of the field or lawn. So, for a straight-sided shape, you just add the lengths of each side to find the perimeter.

PRACTICE

31. Calculate the perimeter of the diagram below:

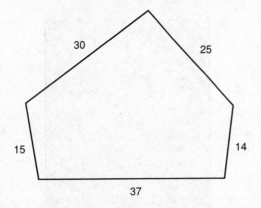

32. Wallpaper borders are decorative strips of wallpaper used to improve the appearance of a room. They are customarily pasted at the top of the wall. After studying the diagram below, how many feet of wallpaper border would you need for the room?

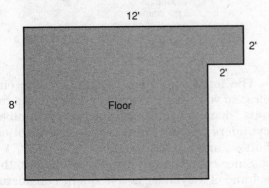

ANSWERS

31. **121 ft; 15 + 30 + 25 + 14 + 37 = 121**
32. **On this diagram there are two unknown lengths to find, 8 – 2 = 6 and 12 – 2 = 10.**

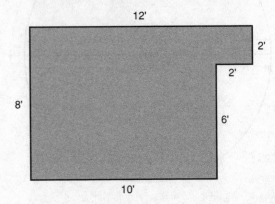

Perimeter = 40; (8 + 12 + 2 + 2 + 6 + 10)

AREA

Area is a term frequently encountered in geometry applications. If you imagine that you are painting the floor of the room you are in, the amount of painted surface is the area of the surface.

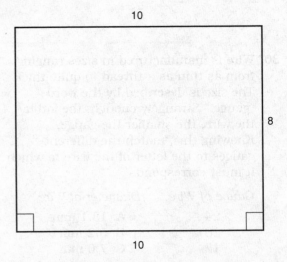

If the above diagram represents the floor that you are painting, to find the area of that floor, you multiply the length by the width. That makes the area 8 times 10, which equals 80.

The units of area are square units, so the floor has an area of 80 square units. If the floor had been measured in feet, the 80 would be called "square feet." The reason for that is that if you could imagine that you were installing tile on the floor and each tile were a square one foot on each side, you could place 80 of these tiles on the floor. You would have 80 square feet of tile.

The idea of area comes up in a large variety of everyday uses, including how much paint to buy, how many bags of lawn fertilizer to spread on your lawn, how much fabric you need for drapes...the list goes on and on.

PRACTICE

Suppose your house and yard have the dimensions and shape shown below.

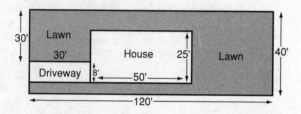

33. How many square feet are in the driveway?

34. How many square feet does the house sit on?

35. How many square feet are in the lawn?

ANSWERS

33. **240; 30 × 8 = 240**
34. **1,250; 50 × 25 = 1,250**
35. **3,310; The area of the lawn is the area of the entire lot minus the area of the dirveway minus the area of the house. This gives (120 × 40) – 240 – 1,250 = 4,800 – 1,490 = 3,310.**

AREA OF A CIRCLE

When you want to compare sizes of pizza, you are considering the area of a circle. Finding the area of a circle is a little bit different from finding the area of a square or a rectangle. You must use a formula. The formula follows:

$A = \pi r^2$, where A = area, $\pi \approx 3.14$, and r = radius

You should practice using this formula until you are very comfortable using it.

PRACTICE

36. Find the area of the circle shown below. Remember that the units of area are square units.

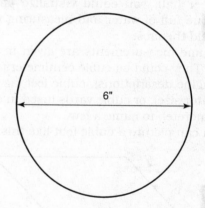

37. Find the area of the circle shown below.

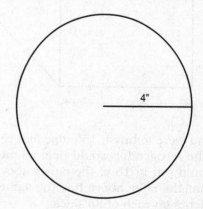

36. **A = π times radius squared**
    A = (3.14)(3)(3)
    A = 28.26 square inches
37. **A = π times radius squared**
    A = (3.14)(4)(4)
    A = 50.24 square inches

VOLUME

The volume of a three-dimensional shape describes how much space it takes up, or how much it could hold if it were a hollow container. For example, if you were comparing the volume of a basketball with the volume of a soccer ball, you could visualize pouring each one full of water and measuring which one held the most.

Volume measurements are given in <u>cubic</u> units. They could be cubic centimeters (as in car engine descriptions), cubic feet (as in refrigerator size), or cubic yards (used in ordering concrete), to name a few.

You can picture a cubic foot like this:

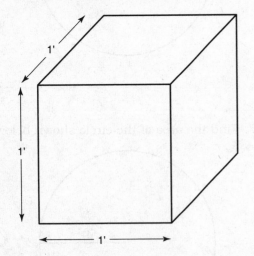

If you were to buy a 15 cubic foot refrigerator, the refrigerator would hold as much as you could put in 15 of the cubes above. Notice that the cube above has the same measurements on each of its sides.

38. Lake Baikal in Russia contains the largest volume of fresh water in the world. It does this even though it does not have nearly the surface area (the part you could see from flying over it) as the Great Lakes of the United States. Which of the following is a conclusion that you could logically draw from just this information?

    (1) Lake Baikal must be spring fed to have so much fresh water.
    (2) Lake Baikal must have a shoreline with many bays and inlets.
    (3) Lake Baikal must be extremely deep.
    (4) The Great Lakes empty into the nearby ocean.
    (5) The Great Lakes have a relatively flat lake bed.

38. **3; If two containers, for example, cylinders, have the same size top, then for one to hold more it must be deeper, so the depth must be greater for Lake Bailal to have a larger volume.**

VOLUME OF A RECTANGULAR SOLID

Anything you can think of that is shaped like a shoe box is a rectangular solid and has a volume that can be found by using this formula:

$$\text{Volume} = \text{length} \times \text{width} \times \text{height}$$
$$\text{or}$$
$$V = l \times w \times h$$

If you measure the three different dimensions and multiply them together, you have found the volume. It really does not matter what you call these three sides, as long as you measure three different dimensions. These dimensions are customarily called length, width, and height.

To find the volume of the rectangular solid shown below, substitute $l = 20$, $w = 8$, and $h = 5$ into the formula to obtain $V = (20)(8)(5) = 800$ cubic units.

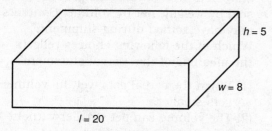

$h = 5$

$w = 8$

$l = 20$

PRACTICE

39. Concrete is sold by the cubic yard, usually referred to simply as "yards." It is the amount of concrete that would fill a box that is l yard long on each of its sides. Suppose you wanted to pour a concrete driveway and parking area as shown below, to a depth of 3 inches ($\frac{1}{12}$ of a yard). How many yards of concrete would you need to order?

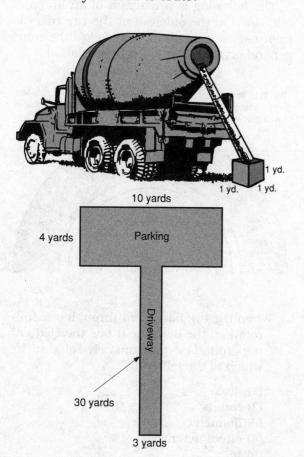

1 yd.

1 yd.   1 yd.

10 yards

4 yards   Parking

Driveway

30 yards

3 yards

39. **10.8; Split the figure into two rectangles as shown below.**

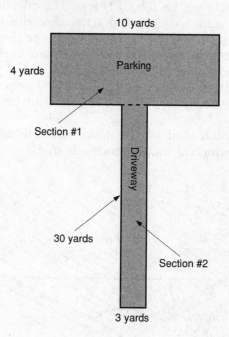

10 yards

4 yards   Parking

Section #1

Driveway

30 yards

Section #2

3 yards

Section # 1
$V = $ **(length)(width)(height)**
$V = (10)(4)(\frac{1}{12})$
$V = 3.33$

Section # 2
$V = $ **(length)(width)(height)**
$V = (30)(3)(\frac{1}{12})$
$V = 7.5$

The total of the two sections is about 10.8 cubic yards

End of Chapter Practice

This practice set is in the same format that you will see on the GED test. The questions are meant to help you practice the skills that you have worked on in this chapter. Try to answer the questions without looking back in the chapter. Mark the ones for which you have to look back for help. This will help you know where to concentrate your studying.

1. After studying the figure below, decide which of the statements is true.

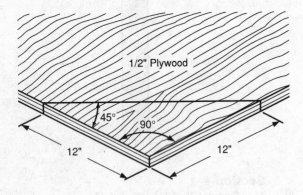

(1) The one angle with no degrees listed will be a 45° angle.
(2) The triangle is a special triangle known as a 3, 4, 5 right triangle.
(3) A triangle with two sides equally long will always have two 45° angles.
(4) Two equally long triangle sides will guarantee that the angle between them is a 90° angle.
(5) The two equally long sides must be parallel.

2. Cereal boxes frequently have a statement that says, "This product is sold by weight, not by volume. Contents may have settled during shipment." Which of the following choices reflects the meaning of that cereal statement?

(1) When the cereal gets wet, its volume gets smaller.
(2) The volume can get smaller without affecting the quantity of cereal.
(3) Volume and weight measure the same things.
(4) The manufacturer is concerned that the size of the box could change during shipment.
(5) The density of the cereal would get smaller as the volume shrinks.

Use the information in this passage to answer questions 3 and 4.

The following is a diagram of an automobile tire. On the sidewall of the tire there is information printed. All tires follow the same general organization of this information.

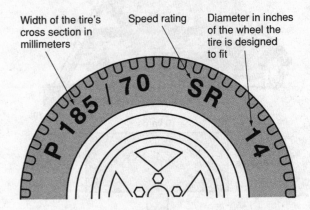

3. When the tire has rolled through one full rotation, the distance it has traveled on the ground is approximately equal to which of the following?

(1) area
(2) radius
(3) diameter
(4) circumference
(5) pi

4. If you bought a tire that was a size P 195/70 SR 14 when its correct size should have been a size P 185/70 SR 13, which of the following would happen?

   (1) The tire would be too big to fit the wheel.
   (2) The tire would be too small to fit the wheel.
   (3) There would be less contact with the road surface.
   (4) The tire would not be correct for a 4 × 4.
   (5) The circumference of the incorrect size would be too small.

5. Which of the following choices is *not* about perimeter?

   (1) The border of a state.
   (2) The waist size for a pair of slacks.
   (3) The double line in the center of the highway.
   (4) The circumference of a circle.
   (5) The shoreline of a lake.

6. On the back of a box of cake mix, the directions include what size pan to use. Suppose the box suggests an 8 inch by 8 inch pan. You try that and your cake turns out well and is $2\frac{1}{2}$ inches high. Approximately how high will the cake be in a 9 inch by 9 inch pan?

   (1) $\frac{1}{2}$ inch
   (2) 1 inch
   (3) $1\frac{1}{2}$ inches
   (4) 2 inches
   (5) $2\frac{1}{2}$ inches

7. A ship leaves port and sails 6 miles west. It then sails 6 miles south, and then 6 miles west again. Approximately how many miles is it from port?

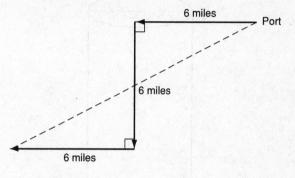

   (1) 9
   (2) 11
   (3) 13
   (4) 15
   (5) 17

Use the following diagram as you answer questions 8 and 9.

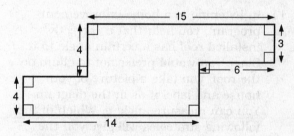

8. What is the perimeter shown in the diagram?

   (1) 46
   (2) 51
   (3) 55
   (4) 56
   (5) Not enough information is given.

9. What is the area (in square units) shown in the diagram?

   (1) 106
   (2) 110
   (3) 116
   (4) 160
   (5) Not enough information is given.

10. If you had a cylinder with the dimensions shown in the diagram, what would be the volume?

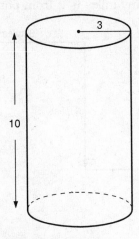

(1) $V = (3.14)(3)(2)(10)$
(2) $V = (3.14)(3.14)(3)(10)$
(3) $V = (3.14)(9)(10)$
(4) $V = (3.14)(3)(100)$
(5) $V = (3.14)(4)(10)$

11. In listening to a home improvement program, you hear that a correctly installed roof has a certain angle to it. Since you would prefer not to climb on the roof, you take a picture of your house and label it as in the diagram. You can measure angle y. Which of the following strategies will give you the value for angle x?

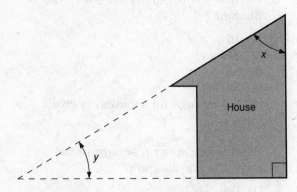

(1) $x = y$
(2) $x = 90 - y$
(3) $x = 180 - y$
(4) $x = 360 - y$
(5) $x = \frac{1}{2}y$

ANSWERS

1. **1** The sum of the angles of a triangle is 180°, so $180 - 45 - 90 = 45$.
2. **2** The cereal manufacturer is saying that the weight will not be changed, even if the amount of cereal looks smaller.
3. **4** The tire rolls on its outer border, which is its circumference, because the tire is circular.
4. **1** Since the 14 is the diameter of the tire, the tire would be too big to fit a wheel that is only 13" in diameter.
5. **3** This is the only choice that doesn't measure the distance around the border of something.
6. **4** The volume of cake batter in the 9" pan will be the same as in the 8" pan. You can then equate the two volumes; letting x represent the height in the 9" pan:

   Volume in 8" pan = Volume in 9" pan

   $$(8)(8)(2\frac{1}{2}) = (9)(9)(x)$$
   $$160 = 81x$$
   $$1.975 = x$$

   Since the answers are listed as approximate values, the 2 inches would be closest.
7. **3** The dotted line is found by applying the Pythagorean relationship. Half of the dotted line would be the square root of $6^2 + 3^2$, or about 6.7. Doubling this gives about 13.
8. **4** The missing horizontal segment has length 5 because the total length across the upper horizontal segments must equal the total length along the lower horizontal segments, and $5 + 15 = 14 + 6$. Likewise, the missing vertical segment has length 5 because $5 + 3 = 4 + 4$.
   Starting in the bottom left corner and traveling clockwise gives Perimeter = $4 + 5 + 4 + 15 + 3 + 6 + 5 + 14 = 56$.

9. 2 Look at the diagram below:

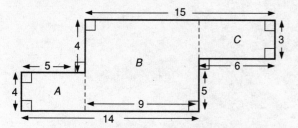

Total area = area of section "A" + area of section "B" + area of section "C"

Area = (5)(4) + (9)(8) + (6)(3)
So, Area = 20 + 72 + 18 = 110 sq. units.

10. 3 The formula for the volume of a cylinder will be given on the GED. It is $V = \pi r^2 h$, where r is the radius and h the height.
So, $V = (3.14)(3)(3)(10)$, since $(3)(3) = 9$.

11. 2 Remember that the total of the angles in a triangle is 180°. So, x will be $180 - 90 - y$ (the 90 came from the little box in the bottom right hand corner that stands for 90°). Subtract the 90 from 180, giving the final answer $90 - y$.

Data Analysis

Data analysis combines common sense and math skills. One of the most common forms of data analysis that you do every day is evaluating advertisements. Whenever you first see an ad for something that interests you, you analyze the content of the ad. For example, suppose that a store is having a "buy one . . . get one free" deal on a product that you like. The analysis that you do is to find out the price of the one you have to buy. If the price is twice the normal price, then the deal is not a deal at all, but just a come-on. So you can see that data analysis is an every-day event and one with which you have practice. In this chapter you will learn how to analyze data in graphs, tables, and statistics.

Graphs

Graphs are found in the daily newspaper, on TV—even in the booklet that you get from the IRS for filing your tax return. You have heard that a picture is worth a thousand words— this is very true for the picture that is a graph. It is a way of telling the reader a lot of information in a picture format. There are three basic kinds of graphs that you will work with here: the line graph, the bar graph, and the pie graph.

AXES

Line graphs and bar graphs have two axes, which are the horizontal and vertical lines that tell you how to read the graph and give you its scale. The axis that runs up and down is called the *y* axis. The axis that runs across is called the *x* axis. These axes are always labeled so that the reader will know what they represent.

LINE GRAPHS

Line graphs are generally used to show a change in measurement. When you examine a line graph—for example, the jagged line that shows the ups and downs of the stock market—it helps to follow the mental steps detailed below. Try this as you examine the line graph that follows these steps.

Step One: Read the words written along the *x* and the *y* axes.
Step Two: Study the numbers, or scales, along the two axes.
Step Three: Form an idea in your mind of what the graph is showing.

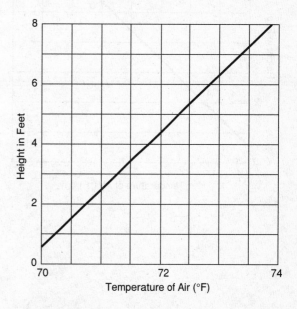

Applying these steps to the graph above, the words along the *x* axis explain that we are measuring the temperature of the air. The words along the *y* axis explain that we are also measuring the height above the floor or above the ground. The numbers on the *x* axis let us know that the temperature range is from 70° to 74°. The numbers on the *y* axis let us know that the heights range from 0 feet to 8 feet.

Now, to decide what the graph is showing, notice that the line is tilted in a certain way. To see what this means, pick two points on the line, as shown below. Any two points will do. Look at point *A* and ask yourself what is happening both to temperature and to height as you move along the graph to point *B*. The answer is that temperature is increasing and height is increasing. From this observation you can decide what the graph is about. You might say that it shows that hot air rises. You might say that the temperature of the air increases as you go up. There is a variety of things that you could say about the graph, but all of them have basically the same meaning.

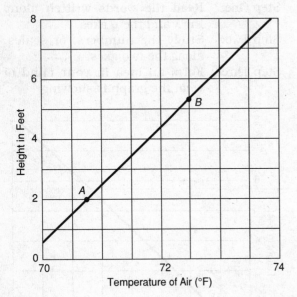

PRACTICE

For each graph below, write a statement describing what the graph shows.

1.

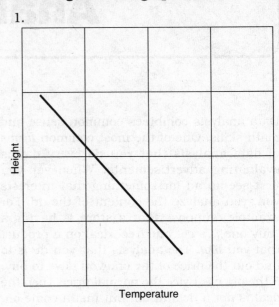

2.

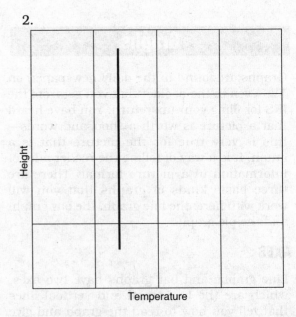

3.

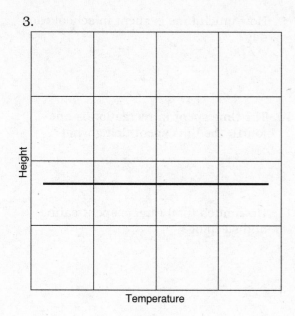

Evaluate the bar graphs below and answer these questions:

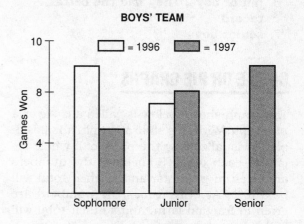

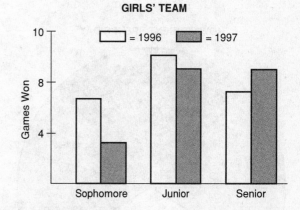

ANSWERS

1. **As the height decreases, the temperature increases, so it is warmest near the floor or ground.**
2. **The temperature is the same for all heights shown.**
3. **This graph shows that at the same height, there is a range of temperatures.**

BAR GRAPHS

Bar graphs are very similar to line graphs. The only real difference is that instead of a line joining all the data (very much like the "connect the dot" type of puzzle), there will be a bar drawn from each data point to the axis. These graphs are an effective way to *compare* measurements.

4. Which boys' team won the most games in 1996?

5. Which junior team was the best in 1997, the boys or the girls?

6. If the 1996 senior boys played the 1997 junior boys, who would probably win?

7. Looking at all six teams, which team improved the most from 1996 to 1997?

4. **sophomore**
5. **girls**
6. **junior boys; They had the better record.**
7. **senior boys**

CIRCLE OR PIE GRAPHS

The graph shown below is called a *circle* or a *pie* graph. With this style of graph, it is possible to visualize how the parts of a whole relate to each other. Sometimes the numbers are given in percents, and so their total will be 100%. At other times the numbers are given in fraction form, and so their total will be 1.

HOW STUDENT SPENDS DAY

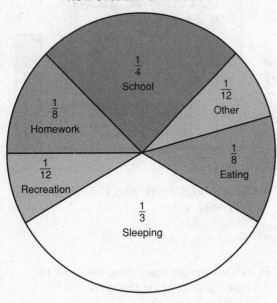

PRACTICE

Use the pie graph above to answer questions 8–11.

8. How does a student spend the largest part of the day?

9. How much time is spent in school each day?

10. The time spent in recreation is one-fourth the time spent doing what?

11. How much total time is spent eating and sleeping?

ANSWERS

8. **sleeping; This is the largest section of the pie.**

9. **6 hours;** $\frac{1}{4}(24 \text{ hours}) = 6 \text{ hours}$

10. **sleeping;** $\frac{1}{4}\left(\frac{1}{2}\right) = \frac{1}{12}$

11. **11 hours;** $\frac{1}{8}(24) + \frac{1}{3}(24) = 3 + 8 = 11$

Analyzing Data

TABLES

A table organizes information in rows and columns. This lets you present a lot of information in a relatively small space, and in a format that allows you to find relationships more easily than if the information were in paragraph or other form. When you examine a table, do not be overwhelmed by its appearance. Take your time, and remember that all the answers you are looking for are right there.

Use the portion of the income tax table shown below to answer Questions 12–14.

If line 37 (taxable income) is—		And you are—			
At least	But less than	Single	Married filing jointly	Married filing sepa-rately	Head of a house-hold
			Your tax is—		
44,000					
44,000	44,050	9,292	7,257	9,792	8,265
44,050	44,100	9,306	7,251	9,806	8,279
44,100	44,150	9,320	7,285	9,280	8,293
44,150	44,200	9,334	7,299	9,834	8,307
44,200	44,250	9,348	7,313	9,848	8,321
44,250	44,300	9,362	7,327	9,862	8,335
44,300	44,350	9,376	7,341	9,876	8,349
44,350	44,400	9,390	7,355	9,890	8,363
44,400	44,450	9,404	7,369	9,904	8,377
44,450	44,500	9,418	7,383	9,918	8,391
44,500	44,550	9,432	7,397	9,932	8,405
44,550	44,600	9,446	7,411	9,946	8,419
44,600	44,650	9,460	7,425	9,960	8,433
44,650	44,700	9,474	7,439	9,974	8,447
44,700	44,750	9,488	7,453	9,988	8,461
44,750	44,800	9,502	7,467	10,002	8,475
44,800	44,850	9,516	7,481	10,016	8,489
44,850	44,900	9,530	7,495	10,030	8,503
44,900	44,950	9,544	7,509	10,044	8,517
44,950	45,000	9,558	7,523	10,058	8,531

12. If your taxable income is $44,748, what would be the tax if you were married filing jointly?

13. If you file as the head of a household and your tax is $8,405, between what two figures is your taxable income?

14. How much tax would a single person pay on a taxable income of $44,732?

12. **$7,453**
13. **between $44,500 and $44,550**
14. **$9,488**

PROBABILITY

We have been using both the terms "data" and "information" in this chapter, but in mathematics, they are practically the same. The word data means a collection of pieces of information. The baseball information below is data organized in a table. We can use this baseball data to look at the idea of probability.

Time at Bat	What Happened (H = hit and O = out)
1	O
2	H
3	O
4	H
5	O
6	O
7	O
8	H
9	O
10	H

When you flip a coin, you expect it to come up heads one out of every two times, on average. That is, the *probability* of heads is $\frac{1}{2}$. The probability of something happening is the number of times you expect it to occur out of the total number of times, or:

$$P = \frac{\text{Number of favorable outcomes}}{\text{Total number of outcomes}}$$

In looking at the baseball data, there are 10 total outcomes (at-bats), while the number of favorable outcomes (hits) is 4. So, the probability of getting a hit is 4 out of 10. This probability can be expressed as the fraction $\frac{4}{10}$, or as the decimal 0.4.

PRACTICE

15. Sam is designing a board game for children. It has 40 squares that you can "land on."

> Hot pink = 8 squares
> Lemon yellow = 2 squares
> Wild blue = 20 squares
> Neon green = 10 squares

(a) What is the probability of landing on a neon green square using the phrase "out of"?

(b) Use a fraction to describe the probability of landing on a hot pink square (remember to reduce).

(c) Use a decimal to describe the probability of landing on a wild blue square.

ANSWERS

15a. **10 out of 40, or reduce it to 1 out of 4; There are 10 favorable squares (neon green) out of the 40 total squares.**

15b. $\dfrac{8}{40} = \dfrac{1}{5}$; **There are 8 hot pink squares; divide this by 40, the total number of squares.**

15c. $\dfrac{20}{40} = 0.5$; **There are 20 wild blue squares; divide this by 40, the total number of squares.**

STATISTICS

Statistics are different measurements that you make of data. For example, the gross national product is a statistic about our economy. Two of the statistics that you will see frequently are the mean, or average, and the median.

THE MEAN

The idea of an average is a familiar one. You have heard of a batting average, and your grades in school were averages. Even credit card balances are calculated as an average balance. The word *mean* is a synonym for average, though you may not see it as often. The average yearly amount of rain in a particular area is called the mean annual rainfall.

To calculate the average, add together all of the values and then divide by the number of these values.

For example, the yearly snowfall in a location is shown in the table below.

Year	Snowfall in Inches
1995	96.1
1994	78.5
1993	70.9
1992	81.0

To calculate the average snowfall, add the yearly snowfalls and divide by the number of years:

$$\text{average (mean)} = \frac{96.1 + 78.5 + 70.9 + 81.0}{4}$$

$$= 81.625$$

PRACTICE

16. Calculate Joe's average lawn mowing income for May through August from the following data.

Month	Income
May	$550.00
June	$725.00
July	$650.00
August	$675.00

17. What is the skier's average time for the downhill based on these times:

> 9 minutes and 3 seconds
> 8 minutes and 30 seconds
> 9 minutes and 54 seconds

ANSWERS

16. **The months' incomes added together = $2,600. Then divide by 4 months to get $650.**
17. **The addition of the times gives 26 minutes and 87 seconds. The 87 seconds is 1 minute and 27 seconds, so the total time is 27 minutes and 27 seconds. Dividing this total by 3 gives an average of 9 minutes and 9 seconds.**

THE MEDIAN

You may also encounter the statistic called the *median* while taking the GED. The median is the middle item in an ordered set of data. To find the median of a set of data, arrange the data from lowest number to highest number. After doing that, if there is an odd number of values, then the median is the middle number. If there is an even number of values, then the median is the average of the two middle numbers.

PRACTICE

18. Find the median weight for this group of puppies. All weights are in pounds.

> 10.5, 9.5, 10.2, 9.4, 10.0, 9.7,
> 9.8, 10.1, 9.9, 10.7

ANSWERS

18. **Step one is to arrange the values from smallest to largest. Since there is an even number of values, the**

median will be the average of the two middle weights, or the fifth and sixth weights. They weigh 9.9 and 10.0 pounds, so the average is 9.95.

USES OF STATISTICAL DATA

Statistical information is an influential component in advertising. For example, you might see an advertisement like this one:

> "8 out of 10 doctors prescribe the ingredient found in Prestige Pills!"

The advertiser is hoping that you will think that 8 out of 10 doctors favor Prestige Pills. If you think about what the ad really says, you will realize that it could be that no doctors actually favor Prestige Pills, but rather they favor other brands that have the same ingredient as that found in Prestige Pills. So, whenever you come across some statistic, read it carefully to see what it is really saying.

PRACTICE

19. Regular coffee is 97% caffeine free. What percent caffeine does it contain?

ANSWERS

19. **3 %; If 100% represents the whole amount of coffee, then 3% must be caffeine if the other 97% is not.**

End of Chapter Practice

1. Jean, age 22, has a job that gives her a take-home paycheck of $1,200 each month. According to the pie graph shown below, which of these statements is true?

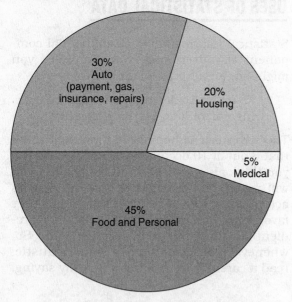

(1) Jean can afford a $360 car payment.
(2) There is no money in Jean's budget for clothes.
(3) Charitable contributions would have to come out of Jean's medical budget.
(4) Jean's rent, including utilities, should not exceed $240 a month.
(5) This budget would also work for a teen living at home.

2. From the *x* axis shown below, what is the correct *x* value for *A*?

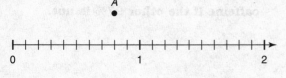

(1) 0.8
(2) $\frac{3}{4}$
(3) 7.5
(4) 8
(5) 16

3. From the *y* axis shown below, what is the correct *y* value for *B*?

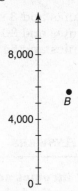

(1) 4,008
(2) 4,080
(3) 4,800
(4) 4,880
(5) 5,800

4. From the race car test drive graph below, which of the following is true?

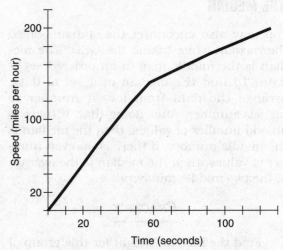

(1) At 10 seconds into the test, the test car was going 40 miles per hour.
(2) When the car's speed reached 100 miles per hour, 30 seconds had elapsed.
(3) After 10 minutes, the car's speed will be nearly 500 miles per hour.
(4) The car can go from 0 to 140 miles per hour in 60 seconds.
(5) The car accelerated at the same rate throughout the test.

5. From the snowfall data graph below, which of these statements is true?

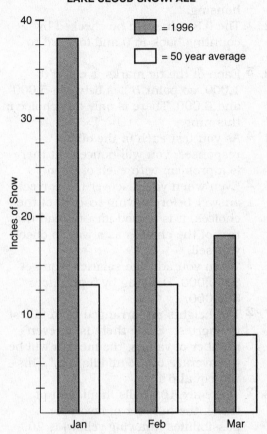

LAKE CLOUD SNOWFALL

= 1996

= 50 year average

Inches of Snow

Jan   Feb   Mar

(1) January is normally the snowiest month in Lake Cloud.
(2) In 1996 the February snowfall was more than the 50 year average.
(3) The January snow average is 16 inches.
(4) Lake-effect snow proved to be Lake Cloud's 1996 trouble.
(5) In February of 1996, 28 inches of snow fell in Lake Cloud.

6. Many retirement plans base their benefit package on the average salary for the last five years worked. What would be Sam's average salary if he had earned these amounts the last five years?

$60,000 $60,000 $50,000

$50,000 $40,000

(1) $45,000
(2) $48,000
(3) $50,000
(4) $52,000
(5) $55,000

7. Calculate the median height of the basketball team with these heights: 6' 10", 6' 9", 6' 7", 6' 5", 6' 3", 6' 2", 6' 1", 6' 0".

(1) 6' 3"
(2) 6' 4"
(3) 6' 4.6"
(4) 6' 5"
(5) 6' 6"

8. The Chamber of Commerce is sponsoring a game at the town carnival. The game box contains the following:

Blue balls: 30
Red balls: 15
Yellow balls: 20
Green balls: 35

What is the probability of getting a yellow ball with one draw?

(1) 0.02
(2) 0.2
(3) 0.5
(4) 1
(5) 2

9. Use the chart of caloric requirements for dogs below to choose the correct response.

CALORIC REQUIREMENTS OF DOGS			
Weight of Dog in Pounds	Calories in Summer	Calories in Winter*	Calories for Growing Puppies**
2	120	180	200
5	250	375	400
10	420	630	700
20	700	1,050	1,200
30	930	1,400	1,400
50	1,350	2,000	2,000
70	1,680	2,500	2,500
100	2,400	3,600	3,600

*Only for dogs living outdoors more than 50% of the time.

**Puppies are considered to be growing until they reach adulthood, or at about 9 to 18 months, depending on breed.

(1) Dogs weighing more than 100 pounds still require 2,400 calories in summer.
(2) A 15 pound dog requires 500 calories a day in summer.
(3) Puppies cannot weigh 100 pounds.
(4) When the weight of the dog doubles, the calorie requirement also doubles.
(5) Calorie requirement is always higher in winter than in summer for outside dogs.

ANSWERS

1. **4** Twenty percent of $1,200 is $240. Utilities certainly fit in the category of housing.
2. **1** The 0.8 value can be checked by counting back to 0 and forward to 1.0.
3. **5** Each of the tic marks is equal to 1,000, so point *B* lies between 5,000 and 6,000. There is only one choice in this range.
4. **4** As you test each of the other responses, you will notice that there is a problem with each of them.
5. **2** Even when you discover the correct answer before having read all of the choices, it is a good idea to read the rest of the choices as a way to check yourself.
6. **4** When you add the salaries, you get $260,000. Dividing by 5 produces $52,000.
7. **2** The heights are arranged from tallest to shortest. Since there is an even number of values, the median will be the average of the middle two. This will equal 6'4".
8. **2** There are 100 balls in all. Out of these, the number of favorable possibilities (drawing yellow) is 20, and $\frac{20}{100} = 0.2$.
9. **5** As you read each of the other choices, you will find there to be some inaccuracy in each.

Practice Tests

As you take this practice test, try to see how it relates to the skills and ideas you have learned and practiced throughout this book. At the end of the practice test there is a chart that lets you relate the questions you missed to the topic in the book that deals with that idea. This way you can travel back for a review of the idea without spending a long time trying to find it. Remember that in order for you to pass the math section of the GED, you do not need to be able to answer every question. The number of questions you have to get right depends on the state where you take the test, but in every case there is a generous allowance for errors.

Take this test as though you were taking the real GED. There is an answer sheet provided for gridding in your answers. Provide your own scratch paper and several pencils. You will be allowed 90 minutes for the math section of the GED, so choose a time for taking this test when you will have an uninterrupted 90 minutes. This strategy will give you a better idea of how ready you are for the test.

The entire math section of the GED is multiple choice. If there is a question that you have trouble with, try to eliminate some of the choices. This will improve your chances of getting the right answer.

Practice Tests

Answer Sheet for Practice Test One

TEST 5: MATHEMATICS

1. ① ② ③ ④ ⑤
2. ① ② ③ ④ ⑤
3. ① ② ③ ④ ⑤
4. ① ② ③ ④ ⑤
5. ① ② ③ ④ ⑤
6. ① ② ③ ④ ⑤
7. ① ② ③ ④ ⑤
8. ① ② ③ ④ ⑤
9. ① ② ③ ④ ⑤
10. ① ② ③ ④ ⑤
11. ① ② ③ ④ ⑤
12. ① ② ③ ④ ⑤
13. ① ② ③ ④ ⑤
14. ① ② ③ ④ ⑤
15. ① ② ③ ④ ⑤
16. ① ② ③ ④ ⑤
17. ① ② ③ ④ ⑤
18. ① ② ③ ④ ⑤
19. ① ② ③ ④ ⑤

20. ① ② ③ ④ ⑤
21. ① ② ③ ④ ⑤
22. ① ② ③ ④ ⑤
23. ① ② ③ ④ ⑤
24. ① ② ③ ④ ⑤
25. ① ② ③ ④ ⑤
26. ① ② ③ ④ ⑤
27. ① ② ③ ④ ⑤
28. ① ② ③ ④ ⑤
29. ① ② ③ ④ ⑤
30. ① ② ③ ④ ⑤
31. ① ② ③ ④ ⑤
32. ① ② ③ ④ ⑤
33. ① ② ③ ④ ⑤
34. ① ② ③ ④ ⑤
35. ① ② ③ ④ ⑤
36. ① ② ③ ④ ⑤
37. ① ② ③ ④ ⑤
38. ① ② ③ ④ ⑤

39. ① ② ③ ④ ⑤
40. ① ② ③ ④ ⑤
41. ① ② ③ ④ ⑤
42. ① ② ③ ④ ⑤
43. ① ② ③ ④ ⑤
44. ① ② ③ ④ ⑤
45. ① ② ③ ④ ⑤
46. ① ② ③ ④ ⑤
47. ① ② ③ ④ ⑤
48. ① ② ③ ④ ⑤
49. ① ② ③ ④ ⑤
50. ① ② ③ ④ ⑤
51. ① ② ③ ④ ⑤
52. ① ② ③ ④ ⑤
53. ① ② ③ ④ ⑤
54. ① ② ③ ④ ⑤
55. ① ② ③ ④ ⑤
56. ① ② ③ ④ ⑤

TEST 5: MATHEMATICS

Tests of General Educational Development
Directions*

The Mathematics Test consists of multiple-choice questions intended to measure general mathematics skills and problem-solving ability. The questions are based on short readings that often include a graph, chart, or figure.

You will have 90 minutes to complete the questions in this test. Work carefully, but do not spend too much time on any one question. Be sure you answer every question. You will not be penalized for incorrect answers.

Formulas you may need are given on page 112. Only some of the questions will require you to use a formula. Not all the formulas given will be needed.

Some questions contain more information than you will need to solve the problem; other questions do not give enough information. If the question does not give enough information to solve the problem, the correct answer choice is "Not enough information is given."

The use of calculators is not allowed.

Do not write in the test booklet. The test administrator will give you blank paper for your calculations. Record your answers on the separate answer sheet provided. Be sure all information is properly recorded on the answer sheet.

To record your answers, fill in the numbered circle on the answer sheet that corresponds to the answer you select for each question in the test booklet.

FOR EXAMPLE:

If a grocery bill totaling $15.75 is paid with a $20.00 bill, how much change should be returned?

(1) $5.26
(2) $4.75
(3) $4.25
(4) $3.75
(5) $3.25

(On Answer Sheet)
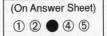

The correct answer is "$4.25"; therefore, answer space 3 would be marked on the answer sheet.

Do not rest the point of your pencil on the answer sheet while you are considering your answer. Make no stray or unnecessary marks. If you change an answer, erase your first mark completely. Mark only <u>one</u> answer space for each question; multiple answers will be scored as incorrect. Do not fold or crease your answer sheet. All test materials must be returned to the test administrator.

DO NOT BEGIN TAKING THE TEST UNTIL TOLD TO DO SO

* Reprinted with permission of the American Council on Education.

TEST 5: MATHEMATICS

FORMULAS*

Description	Formula
AREA (*A*) of a:	
square	$A = s^2$; where s = side
rectangle	$A = \ell w$; where ℓ = length, w = width
parallelogram	$A = bh$; where b = base, h = height
triangle	$A = \frac{1}{2} bh$; where b = base, h = height
circle	$A = \pi r^2$; where r = radius and π is approximately equal to 3.14
PERIMETER (*P*) of a:	
square	$P = 4s$; where s = side
rectangle	$P = 2\ell + 2w$; where ℓ = length, w = width
triangle	$P = a + b + c$; where a, b, and c are the sides
circumference (*C*) of a circle	$C = \pi d$; where d = diameter and π is approximately equal to 3.14
VOLUME (*V*) of a:	
cube	$V = s^3$; where s = side
rectangular container	$V = \ell w h$; where ℓ = length, w = width, h = height
cylinder	$V = \pi r^2 h$; where r = radius, h = height, and π is approximately equal to 3.14
Pythagorean relationship	$c^2 = a^2 + b^2$; where c = hypotenuse, a and b are legs of a right triangle
distance (*d*) between two points in a plane	$d = \sqrt{(x_2 - x_1)^2 + (y_2 - y_1)^2}$; where (x_1, y_1) and (x_2, y_2) are two points in a plane
slope (*m*) of a line	$m = \dfrac{y_2 - y_1}{x_2 - x_1}$; where (x_1, y_1) and (x_2, y_2) are two points on the line
mean	$mean = \dfrac{x_1 + x_2 + \cdots + x_n}{n}$; where the x's are the values for which a mean is desired, and n = number of values for x
median	The *median* is the middle value of an odd number of ordered scores, and halfway between the two middle values of an even number of ordered scores.
simple interest (*i*)	$i = prt$; where p = principal, r = rate, t = time
distance (*d*) as function of rate and time	$d = rt$; where r = rate, t = time
total cost (*c*)	$c = nr$; where n = number of units, r = cost per unit

* Reprinted with permission of the American Council on Education.

TEST 5: MATHEMATICS

<u>Directions:</u> Choose the <u>one best answer</u> to each question.

1. Maps are drawn to scale. The scale used is given on the map. Look at the map below and decide how many miles it is from Oak Grove to Greenville.

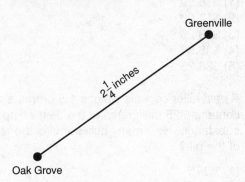

Scale: $\frac{1}{2}$ inch = 10 miles

(1) 40
(2) 42.5
(3) 45
(4) 47.5
(5) 50

2. Calculate John's net pay (also called "take-home pay") from the pay stub shown below. (*Hint:* FICA is the social security tax.)

Gross Pay	$191.60
Federal Income Tax	$28.75
State Income Tax	$3.15
FICA	$19.25

(1) $140.45
(2) $159.70
(3) $162.85
(4) $178.95
(5) $182.10

3. The diagram below is from an automobile owner's manual. It shows the relationship between outside temperature and the recommended oil for the car. Which of these statements is the best conclusion about the diagram?

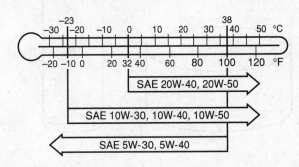

(1) 5W-30 would be the best oil for a hot climate.
(2) 20W-40 would be ideal for winter driving.
(3) Motor oil gets thicker as it gets hotter.
(4) 10W-30 oil is the best choice for temperatures between 10°F and 110°F.
(5) Not enough information is given.

4. Suppose you are considering a job in new car sales. The job description states that the salary is $350 a week plus a commission of 2% on all sales. Calculate your salary for four weeks if you sold 7 cars with a combined price tag of $140,000.

(1) $3,150
(2) $4,200
(3) $28,350
(4) $29,400
(5) Not enough information is given.

GO ON TO THE NEXT PAGE

TEST 5: MATHEMATICS

5. What is the relationship between what the two containers shown below will hold?

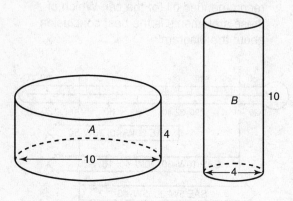

(1) $A > B$
(2) $A < B$
(3) $A = B$
(4) $2A = B$
(5) $2B = A$

6. The temperature at 12:00 noon is −12 degrees F. At 2:00 PM the temperature is 6°F. If the temperature rises at a constant rate, what will be the temperature reading in degrees Fahrenheit at 4 PM?

(1) 14
(2) 16
(3) 20
(4) 24
(5) 30

7. How much will 50 yards of carpet cost at $30.00 a yard if the customer takes advantage of this ad:

Free Carpet:
For every 9 yards you buy, get 1 yard free!!

(1) $1,350
(2) $1,380
(3) $1,410
(4) $1,440
(5) $1,470

8. Sandra makes an item to sell in craft shows. She can make 2 in an hour. Each item has 3 pieces, costing $.50, $.25, and $1.00. If she sells the items for $20.00 each, how much profit is Sandra making per hour?

(1) $16.50
(2) $17.00
(3) $18.25
(4) $36.50
(5) $38.25

9. A pain killer capsule weighs 1.5 grams and contains 325 milligrams of the pain killing substance. How many milligrams is the rest of the pill?

(1) 1.175
(2) 117.50
(3) 175
(4) 1,175
(5) 14,675

10. Many states have a law that states that a person is legally intoxicated with a blood alcohol content of 0.08%. Which of the following is true of that blood alcohol content?

	Parts of Alcohol	Parts of Blood
(1)	8	10
(2)	8	100
(3)	8	1,000
(4)	8	10,000
(5)	8	100,000

GO ON TO THE NEXT PAGE

TEST 5: MATHEMATICS

11. Suppose that one of your favorite foods normally has 300 calories. A "lighter" version appears at the market. It is advertised as having "$\frac{1}{3}$ less calories." How many calories does this "light" version have?

    (1) $299\frac{2}{3}$
    (2) 290
    (3) 270
    (4) 200
    (5) 100

12. If you worked two long days as recorded below, how many total hours did you work?

    Day 1: 13 hours, 43 minutes
    Day 2: 8 hours, 24 minutes

    (1) 21 hours, 7 minutes
    (2) 21 hours, 17 minutes
    (3) 22 hours, 7 minutes
    (4) 22 hours, 17 minutes
    (5) 22 hours, 27 minutes

13. When buying fabric for drapes, the width of the fabric should be $2\frac{1}{2}$ and times the width of the window to allow for pleats. If the width of the fabric is 120 inches, which of these equations could be used to get the width of the window (x)?

    (1) $2.5x = 120$
    (2) $2.5 = 120x$
    (3) $2.5 + x = 120$
    (4) $120 - x = 2.5$
    (5) $(120)(2.5) = x$

14. If you were going to put a door in the wall under the stairs as shown below, which of the following choices would be the set-up for finding the length of x?

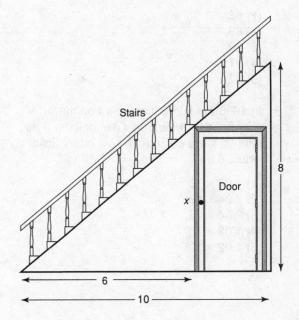

    (1) $\frac{4}{10} = \frac{x}{8}$
    (2) $\frac{6}{4} = \frac{x}{8}$
    (3) $\frac{6}{x} = \frac{8}{10}$
    (4) $\frac{6}{10} = \frac{x}{8}$
    (5) $\frac{x}{6} = \frac{10}{8}$

GO ON TO THE NEXT PAGE

TEST 5: MATHEMATICS

15. The calculation of a golf handicap requires the averaging of the last five games played. What is Rob's average if his last five games were 90, 88, 94, 88, 90?

    (1) 88
    (2) 89
    (3) 90
    (4) 91
    (5) 92

16. In 1996 the interest payment on the national debt was 2.04×10^9 dollars. If this interest were cut in half, how many dollars would it be?

    (1) $1.02 \times 10^{4.5}$
    (2) $2.04 \times 10^{4.5}$
    (3) 2.04×10^7
    (4) 1.02×10^9
    (5) 1.02×10^{11}

17. Highways in hilly country have signs that give the percent of the road's slope. The percent slope is the rise times 100 divided by the run (see the figure below). Which of these diagrams shows a 5% slope?

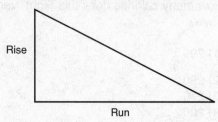

Note: Drawings are not to scale.

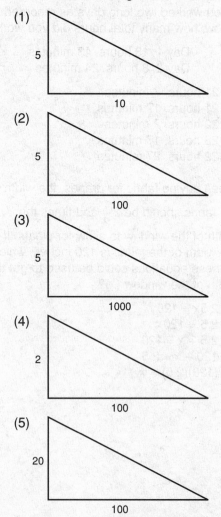

GO ON TO THE NEXT PAGE

TEST 5: MATHEMATICS

18. The phrase "time and a half" for overtime means that the worker receives $1\frac{1}{2}$ times the normal hourly wage for each overtime hour worked. What would the pay be for the week shown below?

    40 hours at $10 per hour
    12 hours at time and a half

    (1) $418
    (2) $520
    (3) $580
    (4) $600
    (5) $780

19. Teachers often have the choice of having their yearly salary spread over 12 months or over 10 months. For a teacher earning $36,000 yearly, what is the difference between the two choices for any month in the school year?

    (1) 50
    (2) 100
    (3) 300
    (4) 600
    (5) 900

20. After evaluating the nutrition labels on the milk labels shown below, which of these is true for 2% milk?

Regular Milk		2% Milk
8 oz.	Serving Size	8 oz.
150	Calories	120
8 grams	Fat	4 grams

    (1) It has 2% of the fat of regular milk.
    (2) It has one-half the fat of regular milk.
    (3) It has 2% of the nutritional value of regular milk.
    (4) It has 2% of the calories of regular milk.
    (5) It has one-half the calories of regular milk.

21. Using the tax schedule below, if the amount on line 37 of your tax return is $40,000, what is the amount of tax you should enter on line 38?

Schedule X—Use if your filing status is **Single**			
If the amount on Form 1040, line 37, is Over—	But not over—	Enter on Form 1040, line 38	of the amount over—
$0	$23,350	.... 15%	$0
23,350	56,550	**$3,502.50 +** 28%	23,350
56,550	117,950	**12,798.50 +** 31%	56,550
117,950	256,500	**31,832.50 +** 36%	117,950
256,500	....	**81,710.50 +** 39.6%	256,500

    (1) $3,502.50
    (2) $4,662.00
    (3) $8,164.50
    (4) $14,702.50
    (5) Not enough information is given.

22. How long would it take an airplane flying at an average speed of 600 miles per hour to travel 2,100 miles?

    (1) 3.00 hours
    (2) 3.25 hours
    (3) 3.50 hours
    (4) 4.00 hours
    (5) 4.25 hours

23. A large can of soup costs $1.59 and serves 3 people. What is the cost per serving?

    (1) $.050
    (2) $.053
    (3) $.50
    (4) $.53
    (5) $.60

GO ON TO THE NEXT PAGE

TEST 5: MATHEMATICS

24. What is 926 rounded to the nearest hundred?

    (1) 900
    (2) 925
    (3) 930
    (4) 950
    (5) 1,000

25. Mr. Richards works five days a week. Each day he spends $.50 for a newspaper, $3.75 for lunch, and $1.75 for transportation. How much does he spend for these expenses per week?

    (1) $25.00
    (2) $26.25
    (3) $27.50
    (4) $28.75
    (5) $30.00

26. How many square inches of wood would be scrap (see striped area in the drawing below) when cutting out the design?

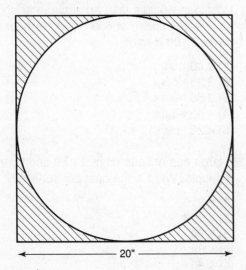

    (1) 20
    (2) 63
    (3) 86
    (4) 100
    (5) Not enough information is given.

27. Phil's retirement benefit package is based on the formula that says that his retirement pay will be 2% of the average annual salary of the last five years times his years of experience. Which of the following will equal his retirement income if he worked 34 years and the average of his last five years' salary is $60,000?

    (1) $3,529
    (2) $6,000
    (3) $12,000
    (4) $40,800
    (5) Not enough information is given.

28. A technique used by quilters is to fold a piece of fabric as shown below. When the cut piece of folded fabric is laid flat, which of these shapes do you get?

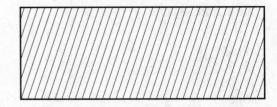

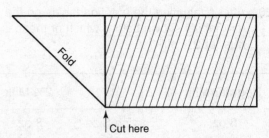

    (1) square
    (2) rectangle
    (3) isosceles triangle
    (4) parallelogram
    (5) trapezoid

GO ON TO THE NEXT PAGE

TEST 5: MATHEMATICS

29. If your insurance premium has been increased from $20 a month to $30 a month, what percent increase is this?

   (1) 10
   (2) 25
   (3) 30
   (4) $33\frac{1}{3}$
   (5) 50

30. Edging for the lawn and garden is available in pound-in pieces that are 4 inches high and 6 inches wide. How many pieces would you need for putting an edge along both sides of a 48 foot path?

   (1) (48)(2)(12)(6)
   (2) $\dfrac{(48)(2)(12)}{6}$
   (3) (48)(12)(6)
   (4) $\dfrac{(48)(12)}{6}$
   (5) $\dfrac{(48)(2)}{6}$

31. In analyzing your budget, a fast food breakfast does not seem like a major financial outlay. How much is your annual breakfast cost if you spend an average of $2.25 each morning for 50 weeks a year, Monday thru Friday?

   (1) $112.50
   (2) $250.00
   (3) $562.50
   (4) $787.50
   (5) $821.25

32. Suppose you were applying for a job with a landscape firm. They want to know if you can handle drawing to scale. If you were to draw the lot shown below, with a scale of $\frac{1}{2}$ inch to equal 10 feet, what would be the dimensions of the lot in inches for your drawing?

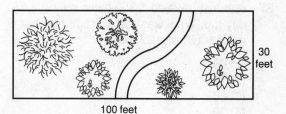

100 feet

30 feet

   (1) 1.0 × 0.3
   (2) 10 × 3
   (3) 3 × 1.5
   (4) 5 × 1.5
   (5) 6 × 20

33. Choose the correct factorization of $2x^2 - x - 21$.

   (1) $(x + 1)(2x - 21)$
   (2) $(x - 1)(2x + 21)$
   (3) $(2x + 7)(x - 3)$
   (4) $(2x - 7)(x + 3)$
   (5) $(2x - 14)(x + 7)$

34. If you are making $10.00 an hour and get a 7% raise, what is your new hourly rate?

   (1) $10.07
   (2) $10.17
   (3) $10.70
   (4) $10.77
   (5) $11.70

35. What is the sum of $3a + 2b + a + 4b$?

   (1) $10ab$
   (2) $3a + 6b$
   (3) $4a + 6b$
   (4) $3a^2 + 6b^2$
   (5) $4a^2 + 8b^2$

GO ON TO THE NEXT PAGE

TEST 5: MATHEMATICS

36. Given the equation $x = 3(y - 2z)^2$, solve for x if $y = 9$ and $z = 3$.

    (1) 9
    (2) 27
    (3) 75
    (4) 81
    (5) 96

37. A tourist traveled 1,350 miles during a 15 day trip. What was the average number of miles traveled each day?

    (1) 60
    (2) 70
    (3) 80
    (4) 90
    (5) 110

38. Fred began work at 8:30 AM. He took a lunch break from 12 noon for a half hour and then finished work at 5 PM. How many hours did he work?

    (1) 7 hours
    (2) 7 hours and 30 minutes
    (3) 8 hours
    (4) 8 hours and 30 minutes
    (5) 9 hours

39. The National Weather Service has issued a storm bulletin stating that a storm is moving at a speed of 35 miles per hour. Its present location is about 100 miles from you, and it is moving in your direction. Approximately how long will it take for the storm to reach you?

    (1) 2 hours
    (2) $2\frac{1}{2}$ hours
    (3) 3 hours
    (4) $3\frac{1}{2}$ hours
    (5) 4 hours

40. Bert's company reimburses him at 32 cents a mile when he uses his car for company business. How much will he be paid for a trip that began with an odometer reading of 30,195 and ended with a reading of 30,640?

    (1) $14.24
    (2) $44.50
    (3) $142.40
    (4) $445.00
    (5) Not enough information is given.

41. If you were setting up a trellis for growing green beans as shown below, how tall would the trellis be (x), given the other dimensions shown.

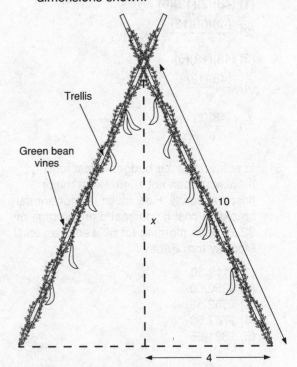

    (1) Between 8 and 9
    (2) Between 9 and 10
    (3) Between 82 and 83
    (4) Between 83 and 84
    (5) Not enough information is given.

GO ON TO THE NEXT PAGE

TEST 5: MATHEMATICS

42. If your health insurance pays 80% of the cost of an office visit, how much did the doctor charge if you had to pay $12.00?

    (1) 15
    (2) 24
    (3) 48
    (4) 60
    (5) 80

43. Many bottles of over-the-counter pain killers have a label stating: "nonprescription strength." From the list of the following, which would be the most likely to be nonprescription strength?

	Number of Pills	Number of Milligrams per Pill
(1)	200	1,000
(2)	50	600
(3)	250	500
(4)	500	325
(5)	100	0

44. The speed of sound is 330 meters per second. The fireworks display is across the river valley from your home. If it takes 10 seconds for the sound to reach you, how many kilometers away is it?

    (1) (10)(330)
    (2) (10)(330)(1,000)
    (3) $\dfrac{(10)(330)}{1,000}$
    (4) (10)(330)(100)
    (5) $\dfrac{(10)(330)}{100}$

45. Mountain Telephone Company charges $1.15 for the first three minutes and 12 cents for each additional minute when calling Denver. What would be the cost of a 23 minute call?

    (1) $2.40
    (2) $2.76
    (3) $3.55
    (4) $3.91
    (5) $23.12

46. Which letter represents the coordinates (3, −3)?

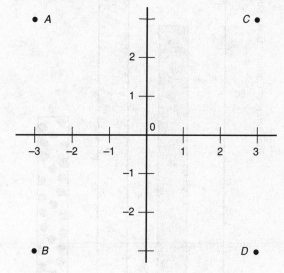

    (1) A
    (2) B
    (3) C
    (4) D
    (5) Not enough information is given.

GO ON TO THE NEXT PAGE

TEST 5: MATHEMATICS

47. From the graph below, which of these conclusions can be drawn?

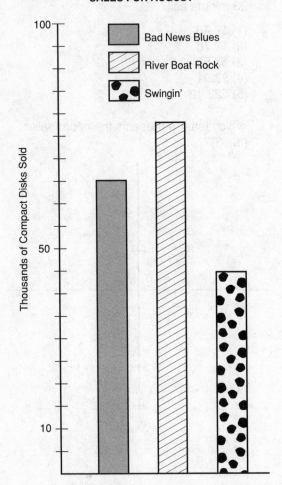

SALES FOR AUGUST

- Bad News Blues
- River Boat Rock
- Swingin'

Thousands of Compact Disks Sold

(1) Bad News Blues gained in popularity through the year.
(2) River Boat Rock outsold Swingin' by 3,300 copies.
(3) Forty thousand copies of Swingin' were sold in August.
(4) Sixty-five thousand copies of Bad News Blues were sold in August.
(5) After an upswing, CD sales declined in August.

48. There is something wrong with this description for mixing plant food with water: 1 teaspoon to the quart or 1 tablespoon to the gallon. Assume that the quart recipe is good. How would you change the gallon recipe? Remember that 3 teaspoons = 1 tablespoon and 4 quarts = 1 gallon.

(1) Use 1 tablespoon and 1 teaspoon of plant food.
(2) Add 1 quart to the 1 gallon of water.
(3) Use 5 teaspoons of plant food.
(4) Use 3 teaspoons of plant food.
(5) The 1 gallon size should not be prepared.

49. Which of these statements accurately describes the rainfall situation in Moose Creek, shown in the graph below?

RAINFALL IN MOOSE CREEK

Rainfall Inches

Jan.   Apr.   July   Oct.   Jan.

(1) April and July are equally rainy months.
(2) January is the driest month.
(3) There were 5 inches of rain in March.
(4) A flash flood occurs with $2\frac{1}{2}$ inches of rain in one hour.
(5) Less than 2 inches of rain in the summer months causes a drought.

GO ON TO THE NEXT PAGE

TEST 5: MATHEMATICS

50. Sally, age 46, wishes to buy a $100,000 life insurance policy. From the table below, what will this coverage cost her for a year?

LIFE INSURANCE PREMIUM COSTS	
Age	**Annual Cost per $1,000**
44	29.50
45	30.15
46	31.50
47	32.85
48	33.50

(1) $31.50
(2) $32.36
(3) $315.00
(4) $323.60
(5) $3,150.00

51. In financing a new car, Stan realizes that he is going to be keeping $10,000 of the bank's money for 2 years. What will be the dollar difference between interest rates of 6.9% and 7.1% for two years?

(1) $20
(2) $40
(3) $200
(4) $400
(5) $2,000

52. Dice are frequently used in board games. Each die has six sides with a different number from 1 through 6 on each side. What is the probability of rolling a 3 on one die?

(1) 0.50
(2) 0.33
(3) 0.25
(4) 0.20
(5) 0.17

53. The label on a box of dog biscuits has the following information:

Dandy Dog Biscuits
Medium—for dogs 20–35 pounds
4 biscuits in morning   3 biscuits at night
Decrease dog food by 25%

Which conclusion can be drawn?

(1) 7 biscuits = 20 to 35 pounds
(2) 4 morning biscuits = 3 evening biscuits
(3) 7 biscuits = $\frac{3}{4}$ dog's calorie needs
(4) 7 biscuits = $\frac{1}{4}$ dog's calorie needs
(5) Not enough information is given.

54. If you plan to leave a 20% tip at dinner, how much should the tip be for a party of four with a bill of $120?

(1) $6.00
(2) $12.00
(3) $18.00
(4) $24.00
(5) $36.00

55. Rainfall is reported in inches. Which of these set-ups will tell the number of pounds of water that would be in your yard after a 1 inch rain, if your yard is 100 feet by 75 feet? One cubic inch of water weighs 0.036 pound.

(1) $100 \times 75 \times 0.036$
(2) $\frac{100 \times 75}{0.036}$
(3) $100 \times 12 \times 75 \times 12 \times 0.036$
(4) $\frac{100 \times 12 \times 75 \times 12}{0.036}$
(5) Not enough information is given.

GO ON TO THE NEXT PAGE

TEST 5: MATHEMATICS

56. Suppose that a socket wrench box overturned, spilling its contents. Which of the following is the correct way to organize the sockets from largest to smallest?

(1) $\dfrac{1}{2}, \dfrac{9}{16}, \dfrac{5}{8}, \dfrac{11}{16}, \dfrac{3}{4}$

(2) $\dfrac{11}{16}, \dfrac{9}{16}, \dfrac{5}{8}, \dfrac{3}{4}, \dfrac{1}{2}$

(3) $\dfrac{3}{4}, \dfrac{5}{8}, \dfrac{11}{16}, \dfrac{9}{16}, \dfrac{1}{2}$

(4) $\dfrac{3}{4}, \dfrac{11}{16}, \dfrac{5}{8}, \dfrac{9}{16}, \dfrac{1}{2}$

(5) $\dfrac{11}{16}, \dfrac{9}{16}, \dfrac{3}{4}, \dfrac{5}{8}, \dfrac{1}{2}$

END OF EXAMINATION

Answer Key

1.	3	11.	4	21.	3	31.	3	41.	2	51.	2
2.	1	12.	3	22.	3	32.	4	42.	4	52.	5
3.	4	13.	1	23.	4	33.	4	43.	4	53.	4
4.	2	14.	4	24.	1	34.	3	44.	3	54.	4
5.	1	15.	3	25.	5	35.	3	45.	3	55.	3
6.	4	16.	4	26.	3	36.	2	46.	4	56.	4
7	1	17.	2	27.	4	37.	4	47.	4		
8.	4	18.	3	28	1	38.	3	48.	1		
9.	4	19.	4	29.	5	39.	3	49.	1		
10.	4	20.	2	30.	2	40.	3	50.	5		

Self-Analysis

WHAT'S YOUR SCORE?

_____right _____wrong

Excellent	51–56
Good	44–50
Fair	38–43

If your score was low, the explanation of the correct answers that follows will help you. You may obtain additional help by reviewing the self-analysis chart that follows.

Did you get at least 38 correct answers? If not, you need more practice for the Mathematics Test. You can improve your performance to Good or Excellent by analyzing your errors. To determine the areas in which you need further study, review the chart that follows. The question numbers from Practice Test One appear in the column to the left. Circle the questions you answered incorrectly. (Unsolved problems are counted as incorrect.) Refer to the Chapter and Chapter Section indicated for each question for additional review.

SELF ANALYSIS CHART

Question	Chapter	Chapter Section	Question	Chapter	Chapter Section
1	3	Types of problems	29	4	Percent
	4	Proportion	30	6	Perimeter
2	3	Types of problems	31	4	Proportion
3	7	Tables		3	Types of problems
4	4	Percent	32	4	Proportion
5	4	Formulas		3	Calculation skills
	6	Shapes	33	4	Factoring
6	3	Types of problems	34	4	Percent
	4	Signed numbers	35	4	Signed nmbers
7	4	Proportion	36	4	Solving equations
8	3	Calculation skills	37	3	Calculation skills
9	5	Metric	38	5	Time measurement
10	4	Percent	39	4	Formulas
11	3	Calculation skills		3	Calculation skills
	4	Translation	40	3	Types of problems
12	5	Time measurement	41	6	Pythagorean relationship
13	4	Translation			
14	6	Similar triangles	42	4	Percent
15	7	Averages	43	5	Weight measurement
16	4	Scientific notation	44	5	Metric
17	6	Slope	45	3	Calculation skills
18	3	Calculation skills	46	4	Coordinate system
19	3	Types of problems	47	7	Graphs
	3	Calculation skills	48	5	Liquid measurement
20	4	Percent	49	7	Graphs
21	7	Tables	50	7	Tables
22	4	Formulas	51	4	Formula
23	3	Calculation skills	52	7	Uses of statistical data
24	3	Calculation skills			
25	3	Types of problems	53	7	Tables
26	6	Shapes	54	4	Percent
		Area	55	5	Conversion factors
27	4	Percent		6	Volume
	3	Calculation skills	56	3	Sequencing
28	6	Shapes			

Answers Explained

1. **3** $2\dfrac{1}{4}$ inches $\times \dfrac{10 \text{ miles}}{\frac{1}{2} \text{ inch}} = 45$ miles

2. **1** Take the gross pay and subtract everything else, because everything else is a tax.

3. **4** As you read the chart, none of the other answers is true.

4. **2** The salary is made of two components:
   $350 per week times 4 weeks = $1,400
   $140,000 times 0.02 = $2,800
   So, the total is $4,200.

5. **1** It is not even necessary to calculate the volumes, but just to set them up to see the relationship. Remember that the radius is half the diameter.

   $V = \pi\,(5)(5)(4)$ for container A
   $V = \pi\,(2)(2)(10)$ for container B

   Not counting π, since it is common to both, you can see that A is 100, while B is 40, so A is larger than B.

6. **4** To find the rate, think of the first time interval, which is two hours (from noon to 2). During this time interval the temperature rose 18 degrees (from −12 to +6). This gives a rate of 9 degrees in 1 hour. Applying this rate to the time from 2 PM to 4 PM gives 18° above the 6° at 2 PM. Then 6 + 18 = 24.

7. **1** If you split the 50 yards into 5 pieces of 10 yards each, you would get 5 free yards, and have to buy 45 yards. Then multiply 45 yards by $30.00 per yard.

8. **4** Sandra has invested in each craft item a total of $1.75. If she makes 2 per hour, she has a cost per hour of $3.50. If she can sell both of them, she makes $40.00 in income. The difference between $40.00 and $3.50 will be her hourly profit.

9. **4** If the pain pill is 1.5 grams, that would be 1,500 milligrams. 1,500 milligrams minus the 325 milligrams for the pain ingredient equals 1,175 milligrams.

10. **4** Since percent means "per 100," this is saying $\dfrac{0.08}{100}$. To get rid of the decimal in the numerator, multiply top and bottom by 100.

11. **4** One third of the 300 calories would be 100 calories. The food has 100 less, so 300 − 100 = 200.

12. **3** When you first start to add, 13 + 8 = 21 hours. Then the total minutes is 43 + 24 = 67 minutes, which is 1 hour and 7 minutes. So, the total time is 22 hours and 7 minutes.

13. **1** Just write the formula the way you would say it . . . 2.5 times the width of the window = 120 inches.

14. **4** Remember in setting up proportions to compare similar parts.

15. **3** The addition of all the scores gives 450. Dividing by the number of scores (5) gives an average of 90.

16. **4** When dividing by 2, the 2.04 becomes 1.02. Since 1.02 is still between 1 and 10, the exponent is not affected.

17. **2** In order to get 5% for the answer, using the formula works only for choice 2, where you would multiply 5 by 100 and then divide by 100.

18. **3** The regular part of the time would be 40 hours times $10 per hour for $400. The overtime part would be 12 hours at $15 per hour for $180. This would make the total pay $580.

19. **4** Take the $36,000 and divide by 10 to get $3,600 per month. Then take $36,000 and divide by 12 to get $3,000 per month.

20. **2** According to the chart, regular milk has 8 grams of fat and 2% milk has 4 grams of fat, or half the fat.

21. **3** The $40,000 fits on the line that says $3,502.50 + 28% of the amount over $23,350. So the tax is the total of two parts, the $3,502.50 plus 0.28 × 16,650.

22. **3** Use the distance formula from the formula page:
    Distance = rate times time
    $2,100 = 600 \times t$

    So, $600t = 2,100$, or $t = 3.5$.

23.**4** $1.59 ÷ 3 = $.53

24.**1** The phrase "rounded to the nearest hundred" means that you would expect only zeroes in the units and tens places. Since the 26 is less than halfway to the next hundred, it will be thrown out, leaving 900.

25.**5** The sum of his daily expenses is $6.00. Since he does this 5 times a week, multiply 6 × 5.

26.**3** The area of the whole square minus the area of the circle will give the area of the striped part. The whole square has area 20 × 20 = 400. The circle's area is (3.14)(10)(10) = 314. Then, 400 – 314 = 86.

27.**4** (60,000)(0.02)(34)

28.**1** You can try this with a piece of paper to see how it works. You could also do this on the real GED, as you will have scratch paper to work with.

29.**5** The increase is $10 and the old cost was $20. Percent is part divided by whole times 100, so 10 divided by 20 is 0.5. Multiplying by 100 gives 50%.

30.**2** You are only intested in the width of the pieces, as their height makes no difference in deciding how many you will need. The 48 foot path is doubled (for doing both sides), changed into inches (times 12), and then divided by the size of each piece.

31.**3** The breakfast cost would need to be multiplied by the number of days in a workweek and then multiplied by the number of weeks in a year.

32.**4** Divide the dimensions by 10 to see how many of the inch segments you will need for each side. Since there are 3 ten foot segments in 30, then 3 times $\frac{1}{2}$ will be $1\frac{1}{2}$. The other dimension is 100, for which there are 10 of the ten foot segments. Ten times $\frac{1}{2}$ is 5.

33.**4** Use the FOIL approach to see that this is the only factorization that works.

34.**3** Seven percent is 0.07 times $10 = $.70. This makes the new rate $10.70.

35.**3** Adding just the a's gives $4a$. Adding just the b's gives $6b$. The a's and the b's cannot be combined, so the answer is $4a + 5b$.

36.**2** Insert the values for each letter in that letter's place in the equation.

37.**4** Divide 1,350 miles by 15 days to get 90 miles per day.

38.**3** From 8:30 to noon is $3\frac{1}{2}$ hours. He went back after lunch at 12:30 and worked to 5, which is $4\frac{1}{2}$ hours. The total hours is $4\frac{1}{2} + 3\frac{1}{2} = 8$.

39.**3** The distance formula can be used. Common sense will also do. 100 miles divided by 35 gives approximately 3 hours.

40.**3** The number of miles driven is the difference in the two odometer readings. Multiply this difference by the 32 cents per mile allowed. (The odometer is the dial on the dashboard that records miles driven.)

41.**2** Substituting in the formula for the Pythagorean relationship gives the following:

$$x^2 + 4^2 = 10^2$$
$$x^2 + 16 = 100$$
$$x^2 = 84$$

Since $9^2 = 81$ and $10^2 = 100$, the answer (the square root of 84) lies between 9 and 10.

42.**4** Use the formula $\% = \dfrac{part \times 100}{whole}$.

So, $20 = \dfrac{(12)(100)}{x}$

Solving for x gives $20x = 1,200$, or $x = 60$. You use 20% instead of 80% because the $12.00 is what you pay, not what the insurance pays.

43.**4** The idea here is to focus on the smallest number of milligrams per pill possible without getting to zero, because the phrase "nonprescription strength" means that it is weak enough that you need no prescription.

44.**3** Distance = rate × time

Distance = $\dfrac{330m}{s} \times 10s$

Distance = 3,300 meters
Divide meters by 1,000 to convert to kilometers.

45.**3** After paying $1.15 for the first three minutes, there are 20 minutes left to pay for at the rate of 12 cents for each minute, or $2.40. Adding the two amounts gives $3.55.

46.**4** Remember that the first number is the *x* and the second is the *y*. The *x* is positive, so that would be to the right of the *y* axis. The *y* is negative, so that would be below the *x* axis.

47.**4** This is the only correct response.

48.**1** Since 1 gallon is 4 times the water of 1 quart, you would expect to use 4 times the plant food of the quart recipe. However, using 1 tablespoon will only give you 3 times the plant food. One more teaspoon would be needed in order to have the right ratio.

49.**1** You could quickly eliminate choices 4 and 5 as having nothing to do with the graph. Choice 1 is the only true statement.

50.**5** The thing to notice about the chart is that the dollar amount given buys only $1,000 of insurance. There are 100 of these thousands in the $100,000, so the premium has to be multiplied by 1,000.

51.**2** The difference in the percent is 0.2% or 0.002 when changed to a decimal. The $10,000 times 0.002 times 2 years = $40.

52.**5** The only favorable outcome out of the 6 possible outcomes is rolling a 3.

Dividing 6 into 1 gives 0.166666, or about 0.17.

53.**4** If the directions say to decrease the dog's food by 25%, that is the same as $\frac{1}{4}$.

54.**4** $120 × 0.20 = $24

55.**3** You can think of a cubic inch as (1 inch)^3, or 1 (inch)(inch)(inch)

$$1 \text{ inch} \times 100 \text{ feet} \times \frac{12 \text{ inches}}{\text{foot}} \times$$

$$75 \text{ feet} \times \frac{12 \text{ inches}}{\text{foot}} \times \frac{0.036 \text{ pounds}}{(\text{inch})(\text{inch})(\text{inch})}$$

All of the feet units cancel, and the inches cancel, so the answer is in pounds, as desired. If you had tried instead to divide by 0.036, the answer would not be in the right units.

56.**4** The easiest system is to take all five of the sockets and change the fractions to a common denominator—16 in this case. This gives:

$$\frac{1}{2} = \frac{8}{16}$$

$$\frac{3}{4} = \frac{12}{16}$$

$$\frac{5}{8} = \frac{10}{16}$$

The other two are already in sixteenths. Once they are all in sixteenths, you just use the numerators to decide the order.

Answer Sheet for Practice Test Two

TEST 5: MATHEMATICS

1. ① ② ③ ④ ⑤	20. ① ② ③ ④ ⑤	39. ① ② ③ ④ ⑤
2. ① ② ③ ④ ⑤	21. ① ② ③ ④ ⑤	40. ① ② ③ ④ ⑤
3. ① ② ③ ④ ⑤	22. ① ② ③ ④ ⑤	41. ① ② ③ ④ ⑤
4. ① ② ③ ④ ⑤	23. ① ② ③ ④ ⑤	42. ① ② ③ ④ ⑤
5. ① ② ③ ④ ⑤	24. ① ② ③ ④ ⑤	43. ① ② ③ ④ ⑤
6. ① ② ③ ④ ⑤	25. ① ② ③ ④ ⑤	44. ① ② ③ ④ ⑤
7. ① ② ③ ④ ⑤	26. ① ② ③ ④ ⑤	45. ① ② ③ ④ ⑤
8. ① ② ③ ④ ⑤	27. ① ② ③ ④ ⑤	46. ① ② ③ ④ ⑤
9. ① ② ③ ④ ⑤	28. ① ② ③ ④ ⑤	47. ① ② ③ ④ ⑤
10. ① ② ③ ④ ⑤	29. ① ② ③ ④ ⑤	48. ① ② ③ ④ ⑤
11. ① ② ③ ④ ⑤	30. ① ② ③ ④ ⑤	49. ① ② ③ ④ ⑤
12. ① ② ③ ④ ⑤	31. ① ② ③ ④ ⑤	50. ① ② ③ ④ ⑤
13. ① ② ③ ④ ⑤	32. ① ② ③ ④ ⑤	51. ① ② ③ ④ ⑤
14. ① ② ③ ④ ⑤	33. ① ② ③ ④ ⑤	52. ① ② ③ ④ ⑤
15. ① ② ③ ④ ⑤	34. ① ② ③ ④ ⑤	53. ① ② ③ ④ ⑤
16. ① ② ③ ④ ⑤	35. ① ② ③ ④ ⑤	54. ① ② ③ ④ ⑤
17. ① ② ③ ④ ⑤	36. ① ② ③ ④ ⑤	55. ① ② ③ ④ ⑤
18. ① ② ③ ④ ⑤	37. ① ② ③ ④ ⑤	56. ① ② ③ ④ ⑤
19. ① ② ③ ④ ⑤	38. ① ② ③ ④ ⑤	

TEST 5: MATHEMATICS

Tests of General Educational Development
Directions*

The Mathematics Test consists of multiple-choice questions intended to measure general mathematics skills and problem-solving ability. The questions are based on short readings that often include a graph, chart, or figure.

You will have 90 minutes to complete the questions in this test. Work carefully, but do not spend too much time on any one question. Be sure you answer every question. You will not be penalized for incorrect answers.

Formulas you may need are given on page 134. Only some of the questions will require you to use a formula. Not all the formulas given will be needed.

Some questions contain more information than you will need to solve the problem; other questions do not give enough information. If the question does not give enough information to solve the problem, the correct answer choice is "Not enough information is given."

The use of calculators is not allowed.

Do not write in the test booklet. The test administrator will give you blank paper for your calculations. Record your answers on the separate answer sheet provided. Be sure all information is properly recorded on the answer sheet.

To record your answers, fill in the numbered circle on the answer sheet that corresponds to the answer you select for each question in the test booklet.

FOR EXAMPLE:

If a grocery bill totaling $15.75 is paid with a $20.00 bill, how much change should be returned?

(1) $5.26
(2) $4.75
(3) $4.25
(4) $3.75
(5) $3.25

(On Answer Sheet)
① ② ● ④ ⑤

The correct answer is "$4.25"; therefore, answer space 3 would be marked on the answer sheet.

Do not rest the point of your pencil on the answer sheet while you are considering your answer. Make no stray or unnecessary marks. If you change an answer, erase your first mark completely. Mark only <u>one</u> answer space for each question; multiple answers will be scored as incorrect. Do not fold or crease your answer sheet. All test materials must be returned to the test administrator.

DO NOT BEGIN TAKING THE TEST UNTIL TOLD TO DO SO

* Reprinted with permission of the American Council on Education.

TEST 5: MATHEMATICS

FORMULAS*

Description	Formula
AREA (*A*) of a:	
square	$A = s^2$; where s = side
rectangle	$A = \ell w$; where ℓ = length, w = width
parallelogram	$A = bh$; where b = base, h = height
triangle	$A = \frac{1}{2} bh$; where b = base, h = height
circle	$A = \pi r^2$; where r = radius and π is approximately equal to 3.14
PERIMETER (*P*) of a:	
square	$P = 4s$; where s = side
rectangle	$P = 2\ell + 2w$; where ℓ = length, w = width
triangle	$P = a + b + c$; where a, b, and c are the sides
circumference (*C*) of a circle	$C = \pi d$; where d = diameter and π is approximately equal to 3.14
VOLUME (*V*) of a:	
cube	$V = s^3$; where s = side
rectangular container	$V = \ell w h$; where ℓ = length, w = width, h = height
cylinder	$V = \pi r^2 h$; where r = radius, h = height, and π is approximately equal to 3.14
Pythagorean relationship	$c^2 = a^2 + b^2$; where c = hypotenuse, a and b are legs of a right triangle
distance (*d*) between two points in a plane	$d = \sqrt{(x_2 - x_1)^2 + (y_2 - y_1)^2}$; where (x_1, y_1) and (x_2, y_2) are two points in a plane
slope (*m*) of a line	$m = \dfrac{y_2 - y_1}{x_2 - x_1}$; where (x_1, y_1) and (x_2, y_2) are two points on the line
mean	$mean = \dfrac{x_1 + x_2 + \cdots + x_n}{n}$; where the x's are the values for which a mean is desired, and n = number of values for x
median	The *median* is the middle value of an odd number of ordered scores, and halfway between the two middle values of an even number of ordered scores.
simple interest (*i*)	$i = prt$; where p = principal, r = rate, t = time
distance (*d*) as function of rate and time	$d = rt$; where r = rate, t = time
total cost (*c*)	$c = nr$; where n = number of units, r = cost per unit

* Reprinted with permission of the American Council on Education.

TEST 5: MATHEMATICS

Directions: Choose the <u>one best answer</u> to each question.

1. On 5 successive days a deliveryman listed his mileage as follows: 135, 162, 98, 117, 203. If his truck averages 14 miles for each gallon of gas used, approximately how many gallons of gas did he use during these 5 days?

    (1) 42
    (2) 51
    (3) 115
    (4) 147
    (5) 153

2. Parking meters in Springfield read: "12 minutes for 5¢. Maximum deposit 50¢." What is the maximum time allowed for a driver to be legally parked at one of these meters?

    (1) 1 hour
    (2) 1.2 hours
    (3) 12 hours
    (4) 2 hours
    (5) Not enough information is given.

3. In the triangle below, if $AB = AC$ and m $\angle A$ = 100°, what is the measure of $\angle B$?

    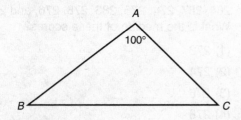

    (1) 40°
    (2) 45°
    (3) 50°
    (4) 60°
    (5) 80°

4. The ABC Department Store had a special sale on shirts. One group sold at $15 per shirt and another group sold at $18 per shirt. If 432 shirts were sold at $15 each and 368 shirts were sold at $18 each the number of dollars taken in at the shirt sale may be represented as

    (1) 800(15 + 18)
    (2) (15)(368) + (18)(432)
    (3) (15)(800) + (18)(800)
    (4) 33(432 + 68)
    (5) (15)(432) + (368)(18)

5. A hockey team won X games, lost Y games, and tied Z games. What part of the games played were won?

    (1) $\dfrac{X}{X + Y + Z}$

    (2) $\dfrac{X}{XYZ}$

    (3) $\dfrac{X}{XY}$

    (4) $\dfrac{X}{X + Y}$

    (5) $\dfrac{X}{X + Y + Z}$

GO ON TO THE NEXT PAGE

TEST 5: MATHEMATICS

6. One-half the students at Madison High School walk to school. One-fourth of the remainder go to school by bicycle. What part of the school population travels by some other means?

   (1) $\dfrac{1}{8}$

   (2) $\dfrac{3}{8}$

   (3) $\dfrac{3}{4}$

   (4) $\dfrac{1}{4}$

   (5) Not enough information is given.

7. For which value of x is the inequality $2x > 9$ true?

   (1) 0

   (2) 2

   (3) 3

   (4) 4

   (5) 5

8. The distance between New York and San Francisco is approximately 3,800

   (1) meters

   (2) kilometers

   (3) kilograms

   (4) liters

   (5) centimeters

9. A flagpole casts a shadow of 16 feet. At the same time, a pole 9 feet high casts a shadow of 6 feet. What is the height of the flagpole, in feet?

   (1) 18

   (2) 19

   (3) 20

   (4) 24

   (5) Not enough information is given.

10. Martin has a piece of lumber 9 feet 8 inches long. He wishes to cut it into 4 equal lengths. How far from the edge should he make the first cut?

    (1) 2.5 feet

    (2) 2 feet 5 inches

    (3) 2.9 feet

    (4) 29 feet

    (5) 116 inches

11. A purse contains 6 nickels, 5 dimes, and 8 quarters. If one coin is drawn at random from the purse, what is the probability that the coin drawn is a dime?

    (1) $\dfrac{5}{19}$

    (2) $\dfrac{5}{14}$

    (3) $\dfrac{5}{8}$

    (4) $\dfrac{5}{6}$

    (5) $\dfrac{19}{5}$

12. The leaders in the Peninsula Golf Tournament finished with scores of 272, 284, 287, 274, 275, 283, 278, 276, and 281. What is the median of these scores?

    (1) 273

    (2) 274

    (3) 276

    (4) 278

    (5) 280

13. The cost of a dozen ball point pens and 8 pencils is $4.60. If the cost of the pens is 3 for $.97, what is the cost of one pencil, in cents?

    (1) 8

    (2) 8.5

    (3) 9.5

    (4) 6

    (5) 9

GO ON TO THE NEXT PAGE

TEST 5: MATHEMATICS

14. The scale on a map is 1 inch = 150 miles. The cities of Benton and Dover are $3\frac{1}{2}$ inches apart on this map. What is the distance between Benton and Dover in miles?

    (1) 525
    (2) 545
    (3) 580
    (4) 625
    (5) Not enough information is given.

15. What is the perimeter of the figure shown below?

    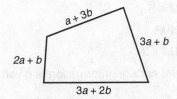

    (1) $8a + 5b$
    (2) $9a + 7b$
    (3) $7a + 5b$
    (4) $6a + 6b$
    (5) $8a + 6b$

16. On the number line below, what is the coordinate of the midpoint of $\overline{AB}$?

    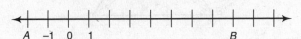

    (1) −11
    (2) 0
    (3) 2
    (4) 3
    (5) 8

17. The Men's Shop advertised a spring sale. David Morris was especially interested in the following sale items.

    3 ties for $23, or $8 each
    3 shirts for $43, or $15 each
    slacks $32.75 each pair
    jackets $58.45 each

    David bought 6 ties, 3 shirts, 2 pairs of slacks, and one jacket. What was his bill?

    (1) $157.20
    (2) $180.20
    (3) $189.95
    (4) $202.95
    (5) $212.95

18. Consider the following arrangements of the given set of numbers.

    A. .80, 19%, .080, $\frac{1}{2}$, $\frac{3}{5}$

    B. .80, $\frac{1}{2}$, .080, $\frac{3}{5}$, 19%

    C. .80, $\frac{3}{5}$, $\frac{1}{2}$, 19%, .080

    D. $\frac{1}{2}$, .80, $\frac{3}{5}$, 19%, .080

    E. $\frac{3}{5}$, $\frac{1}{2}$, 19%, .080, .80

    Which one of the above arrangements places the numbers in order from the greatest to the smallest?

    (1) A
    (2) B
    (3) C
    (4) D
    (5) E

GO ON TO THE NEXT PAGE

TEST 5: MATHEMATICS

19. If an airplane completes its flight of 1,364 miles in 5 hours and 30 minutes, what is its average speed, in miles per hour?

    (1) 240
    (2) 244
    (3) 248
    (4) 250
    (5) 260

20. The distance between two heavenly bodies is 85,000,000,000 miles. This number, written in scientific notation, is

    (1) 8.5×10^{-10}
    (2) 8.5×10^{10}
    (3) 85×10^{9}
    (4) $.85 \times 10^{-9}$
    (5) 850×10^{7}

21. What is the value of $3ab - x^2y$ if $a = 4$, $b = 5$, $y = 3$, and $x = 2$?

    (1) 18
    (2) 24
    (3) 48
    (4) 54
    (5) 72

Questions 22 and 23 are based on the following graph.

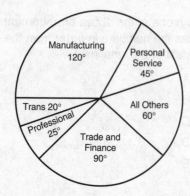

This circle graph shows how 180,000 wage earners in a certain city earned their living during a given period.

22. The number of persons engaged in transportation in the city during this period was

    (1) 3,600
    (2) 9,000
    (3) 10,000
    (4) 18,000
    (5) 36,000

23. If the number of persons in trade and finance is represented by M, then the number in manufacturing is represented as

    (1) $M \div 3$
    (2) $M + 3$
    (3) $30M$
    (4) $4M \div 3$
    (5) Not enough information is given.

---

24. In the triangle below, if $\overline{BF}$ bisects $\angle ABC$, $\overline{CD}$ bisects $\angle ACB$, m$\angle ABC = 68°$, and m$\angle ACB = 72°$, then m$\angle BEC =$

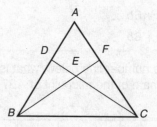

    (1) 90°
    (2) 98°
    (3) 100°
    (4) 110°
    (5) 120°

GO ON TO THE NEXT PAGE

TEST 5: MATHEMATICS

25. Bill has $5 more than Jack, and Jack has $3 less than Frank. If Frank has $30, how many dollars does Bill have?

    (1) $30
    (2) $27
    (3) $32
    (4) $36
    (5) Not enough information is given.

26. John Davis weighed 192 pounds. His doctor put him on a diet, which enabled him to lose at least 4 pounds per month. What was John's weight after 6 months on the diet?

    (1) 160 pounds
    (2) 165 pounds
    (3) 167 pounds
    (4) 168 pounds
    (5) Not enough information is given.

27. Mr. Ames bought a bond for $10,000. The bond yields interest at $8\frac{1}{2}$% annually. If the interest is paid semi-annually, how much is Mr. Ames paid every six months?

    (1) $400
    (2) $425
    (3) $475
    (4) $500
    (5) $850

28. An aquarium is in the form of a rectangular solid. The aquarium is 3 feet long, 1 foot 10 inches wide, and 1 foot 2 inches high. If 1 gallon of water is contained in 231 cubic inches, how many gallons of water are needed to fill the aquarium?

    (1) 24
    (2) 25.8
    (3) 36
    (4) 40
    (5) 48

29. The ratio of men to women at a professional meeting was 9:2. If there were 12 women at the meeting, how many men were at the meeting?

    (1) 33
    (2) 44
    (3) 54
    (4) 66
    (5) Not enough information is given.

30. What is the slope of the line joining point *A* (2,1) and point *B* (4,7)?

    (1) $\frac{1}{3}$

    (2) $\frac{2}{3}$

    (3) $\frac{3}{2}$

    (4) 2

    (5) 3

31. In a basketball game Bill scored three times as many points as Jim. The sum of the scores of Bill and Jim was 56 points. How many points did Bill score ?

    (1) 14
    (2) 28
    (3) 42
    (4) 48
    (5) Not enough information is given.

GO ON TO THE NEXT PAGE

TEST 5: MATHEMATICS

Questions 32 and 33 are based on the following table.

ANNUAL PREMIUM AND INSTALLMENT PAYMENTS PER $1,000 ON ORDINARY LIFE INSURANCE AT AGES FROM 21 THROUGH 25

Age	Annual Premium	Semiannual Installment	Quarterly Installment
21	$16.62	$8.48	$4.32
22	17.08	8.71	4.44
23	17.55	8.95	4.56
24	18.04	9.20	4.69
25	18.56	9.47	4.83

According to the schedule, Michael (age 24) decides to make quarterly payments on a $10,000 policy, while Philip (age 25) decides to make semi-annual payments on his $10,000 policy.

32. How much does Michael pay per year for his $10,000 policy?

    (1) $18.76
    (2) $182.40
    (3) $184.00
    (4) $187.60
    (5) $193.20

33. How much does Philip pay for his policy over a 5-year period?

    (1) $947.00
    (2) $950.00
    (3) $966.00
    (4) $968.00
    (5) $970.50

34. If one pencil cost y cents, then 6 pencils will cost

    (1) $6y$

    (2) $\dfrac{y}{6}$

    (3) $\dfrac{6}{y}$

    (4) $y + 6$

    (5) $\dfrac{y}{2}$

35. One week Mr. Martin worked 42 hours and earned $12 per hour. The following week Mr. Martin worked 37 hours and earned $12 per hour. Which of the following indicates the number of dollars Mr. Martin earned for the two weeks?

    (1) $12 \times 2 + 37$
    (2) $12 \times 42 + 42 \times 37$
    (3) $12 \times 37 + 42$
    (4) $12 + 42 \times 37$
    (5) $12(42 + 37)$

GO ON TO THE NEXT PAGE

TEST 5: MATHEMATICS

36. The enrollment of a college is distributed as follows:

    360 freshmen
    300 sophomores
    280 juniors
    260 seniors

    The freshman class makes up what percent of the total enrollment?

    (1) 18%

    (2) 20%

    (3) 25%

    (4) 30%

    (5) Not enough information is given.

37. In the figure below, $\overleftrightarrow{AB}$ ∥ $\overleftrightarrow{CD}$, $\overleftrightarrow{CE}$ bisects ∠BCD, and m∠ABC = 112°. Find m∠ECD.

    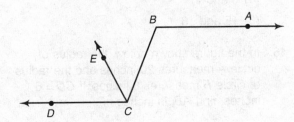

    (1) 45°

    (2) 50°

    (3) 56°

    (4) 60°

    (5) Not enough information is given.

38. Mrs. Garvin buys a bolt of cloth 22 ft. 4 in. in length. She cuts the bolt into four equal pieces to make drapes. What is the length of each drape?

    (1) 5 ft.

    (2) 5 ft. 7 in.

    (3) 5 ft. 9 in.

    (4) 6 ft. 7 in.

    (5) Not enough information is given.

Questions 39 and 40 are based on the following graph.

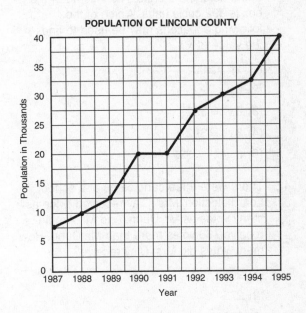

The graph shows the growth in population in Lincoln County between the years 1987 and 1995.

39. What was the population of Lincoln County in the year 1992?

    (1) 20,000

    (2) 25,000

    (3) 26,000

    (4) 27,500

    (5) 30,000

40. The population of Lincoln County did not change between the years

    (1) 1988 and 1989

    (2) 1989 and 1990

    (3) 1990 and 1991

    (4) 1991 and 1992

    (5) 1992 and 1993

GO ON TO THE NEXT PAGE

TEST 5: MATHEMATICS

41. A box is in the form of a rectangular solid with a square base of side x units in length and a height of 8 units. The volume of the box is 392 cubic units. Which of the following equations may be used to find the value of x?

    (1) $x^2 = 392$
    (2) $8x = 392$
    (3) $8x^3 = 392$
    (4) $8x^2 = 392$
    (5) $8 + x^2 = 392$

42. There were three candidates at a school board election. Mrs. Clay received twice as many votes as Mr. Dunn. And Mr. Arnold received 66 votes more than Mr. Dunn. How many votes did Mrs. Clay receive?

    (1) 209
    (2) 275
    (3) 320
    (4) 402
    (5) Not enough information is given.

43. In the triangle below, if $AB = AC$, $\overline{AD} \perp \overline{BC}$, and $m\angle B = 68°$, find $m\angle x$.

    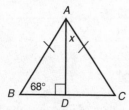

    (1) 10°
    (2) 22°
    (3) 44°
    (4) 50°
    (5) 68°

44. A hiker walks 12 miles due north. Then he turns and walks 16 miles due east. At this point, how many miles is the hiker from his starting point?

    (1) 12
    (2) 16
    (3) 18
    (4) 20
    (5) Not enough information is given.

45. The square root of 30 is between which of the following pairs of numbers?

    (1) 3 and 4
    (2) 4 and 5
    (3) 5 and 6
    (4) 6 and 7
    (5) 15 and 16

46. In the figure shown below, the radius of circle A measures 20 inches and the radius of circle B measures 8 inches. If $CD = 6$ inches, find AB, in inches.

    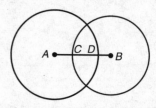

    (1) 22
    (2) 24
    (3) 25
    (4) 28
    (5) Not enough information is given.

GO ON TO THE NEXT PAGE

TEST 5: MATHEMATICS

47. In the figure below, $\overleftrightarrow{CF}$ and $\overleftrightarrow{ED}$ intersect at B, m∠EBF = 50° and $\overleftrightarrow{CB}$ bisects ∠ABD. Find m∠ABC.

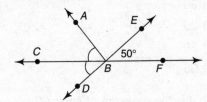

   (1) 30°
   (2) 32°
   (3) 40°
   (4) 50°
   (5) 60°

48. A woman buys *n* pounds of sugar at *c* cents a pound. She gives the clerk a $1.00 bill. The change she receives, in cents, is

   (1) $nc - 100$
   (2) $n + c - 100$
   (3) $100 - (n + c)$
   (4) $100 - nc$
   (5) Not enough information is given.

49. In a high school graduating class 85% of the class planned to go to college. If 170 graduates planned to go to college, how many students were in the graduating class?

   (1) 200
   (2) 250
   (3) 340
   (4) 400
   (5) 500

50. Mr. Denby planned to build a house on the plot of ground shown in the figure below. What is the area of this plot of ground, in square feet?

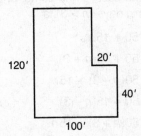

   (1) 10,000
   (2) 10,400
   (3) 10,800
   (4) 12,000
   (5) 104,000

51. If $x = 10$, each of the following is true EXCEPT

   (1) $3x + 1 > 12$
   (2) $2x - 3 < 25$
   (3) $x^2 + 1 > x^2 - 1$
   (4) $4x - 1 = 39$
   (5) $2x - 7 < 7 - 2x$

52. In a right triangle the measure of one acute angle is 4 times as great as the measure of the other acute angle. What is the measure of the larger acute angle?

   (1) 18°
   (2) 36°
   (3) 40°
   (4) 65°
   (5) 72°

GO ON TO THE NEXT PAGE

TEST 5: MATHEMATICS

53. The cost of borrowing a book from a circulating library is $.50 for the first 3 days and $.15 per day after the first 3 days. The minimum number of days is 3. A formula for finding the cost (C), in cents, of borrowing a book for n days ($n \geq 3$) is

    (1) $C = 50 + 15n$
    (2) $C = 50 + 15(n + 3)$
    (3) $C = 50(n - 3) + 15n$
    (4) $C = 50 + 15(n - 3)$
    (5) $C = 50(n + 3) + 15n$

Questions 54 and 55 are based on the following information.

In the figure below line PQ is parallel to line RS.

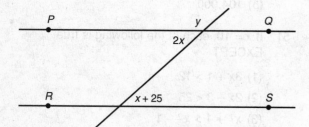

54. What is the value of x?

    (1) 15
    (2) 20
    (3) 25
    (4) 30
    (5) 35

55. What is the measure of angle y?

    (1) 130°
    (2) 135°
    (3) 140°
    (4) 145°
    (5) Not enough information is given.

56. Given the equation $x^2 - x - 12 = 0$, which of the following choices give(s) a complete solution of the equation?
    A. 4   B. –4   C. 3   D. –3

    (1) A only
    (2) B only
    (3) A and C
    (4) A and D
    (5) B and C

END OF EXAMINATION

Answer Key

1. 2	11. 1	21. 3	31. 3	41. 4	51. 5
2. 4	12. 4	22. 3	32. 4	42. 5	52. 5
3. 1	13. 5	23. 4	33. 1	43. 2	53. 4
4. 5	14. 1	24. 4	34. 1	44. 4	54. 3
5. 1	15. 2	25. 3	35. 5	45. 3	55. 1
6. 2	16. 4	26. 5	36. 4	46. 1	56. 4
7. 5	17. 5	27. 2	37. 3	47. 4	
8. 2	18. 3	28. 5	38. 2	48. 4	
9. 4	19. 3	29. 3	39. 4	49. 1	
10. 2	20. 2	30. 5	40. 3	50. 2	

Self-Analysis

WHAT'S YOUR SCORE?

_____right _____wrong

Excellent	51–56
Good	44–50
Fair	38–43

If your score was low, the explanation of the correct answers that follows will help you. You may obtain additional help by reviewing the self-analysis chart that follows.

Did you get at least 38 correct answers? If not, you need more practice for the Mathematics Test. You can improve your performance to Good or Excellent by analyzing your errors. To determine the areas in which you need further study, review the chart that follows. The question numbers from Practice Test Two appear in the column to the left. Circle the questions you answered incorrectly. (Unsolved problems are counted as incorrect.) Refer to the Chapter and Chapter Section indicated for each question for additional review.

SELF-ANALYSIS CHART

Question	Chapter	Chapter Section	Question	Chapter	Chapter Section
1	5	Conversion factors	31	4	Translation
2	5	Conversion factors			Solving equations
3	6	Shapes	32	7	Tables
4	4	Translation	33	3	Calculation skills
5	4	Translation	34	4	Translation
6	3	Types of problems	35	4	Translation
7	4	Inequalities	36	4	Percent
8	5	Metric	37	6	Lines and angles
9	6	Shapes	38	5	Linear measurement
10	5	Conversion factors	39	7	Graphs
11	7	Analyzing data	40	7	Graphs
12	7	Analyzing data	41	6	Shapes
13	4	Translation		4	Translation
		Solving equations	42	4	Translation
14	5	Conversion factors			Solving equations
15	6	Shapes	43	6	Shapes
16	6	Coordinates	44	6	Pythagorean
17	3	Types of problems			relationship
18		Sequencing	45	3	Types of problems
19	3	Calculation skills	46	6	Shapes
20	4	Scientific notation	47	6	Lines and angles
21	4	Substitution	48	4	Translation
22	7	Graphs	49	4	Percent
23	7	Graphs	50	6	Shapes
24	6	Shapes	51	4	Inequalities
25	4	Translation	52	6	Shapes
		Solving equations		4	Translation
26	5	Conversion factors	53	4	Translation
27	3	Types of problems	54	6	Lines and angles
28	6	Shapes	55	6	Lines and angles
29	4	Proportion	56	4	Factoring
30	6	Coordinates			
	4	Substitution			

Answers Explained

1. 2 We first find the total mileage.

135 + 162 + 98 + 117 + 203 = 715 miles.

If we divide the total mileage (715) by the number of miles covered for each gallon of gas used (14) we will find the number of gallons of gas needed.

715 ÷ 14 = 51 gallons to the nearest gallon.

2. 4 5 cents will pay for 12 minutes. $.50 will pay for 10 × 12 = 120 minutes. 120 minutes = 2 hours.

3. 1 If $AB = AC$ then $\triangle ABC$ is an isosceles triangle and the base angles have equal measures.
That is, m∠B = m∠C.
Let x = m∠B = m∠C.

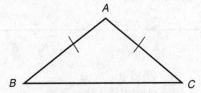

Since the sum of the measures of the angles of a triangle is 180° we have the equation

$$x + x + 100 = 180$$
$$2x + 100 = 180$$
$$2x = 180 - 100 = 80$$
$$x = 40$$

4. 5 Since 432 shirts were sold at $15 each the number of dollars taken in was 15 × 432, or 432 × 15.
Since 368 shirts were sold at $18 each the number of dollars taken in was 18 × 368, or 368 × 18.
The total amount taken in was 15 × 432 + 18 × 368. This may be written as (15)(432) + (368)(18).

5. 1 The total number of games played was $x + y + z$.
The number of games won was x.
The part of the games won was

$$\frac{x}{x + y + z}.$$

6. 2 $\frac{1}{2}$ of the pupils walk to school.
$1 - \frac{1}{2} = \frac{1}{2}$ of the pupils represents the remainder.

$\frac{1}{4}$ of the remainder $= \frac{1}{4} \times \frac{1}{2} = \frac{1}{8}$

of the pupils use bicycles.

$$\frac{1}{2} = \frac{4}{8}$$

$\frac{4}{8} + \frac{1}{8} = \frac{5}{8}$ of the pupils either

walk or use bicycles.

Therefore, $1 - \frac{5}{8} = \frac{3}{8}$ use other

means.

7. 5 $2x > 9$. If we divide both sides of this inequality by 2 we have $x > \frac{9}{2}$,

or $4\frac{1}{2}$.

The only choice that is greater

than $4\frac{1}{2}$ is 5.

An alternate method is to replace x by each of the choices given. The only choice that makes the inequality true is $x = 5$.

8. 2 The distance between New York and San Francisco is approximately 2,500 miles. To express this distance in the metric system we select the

kilometer which is approximately $\frac{5}{8}$

of a mile.
The kilometer is the largest distance unit of the choices given.

9. 4 Let x = height of flagpole.
Since the triangles are similar the lengths of corresponding sides are in proportion.
We use the proportion

$$\frac{h \text{ (flagpole)}}{h \text{ (pole)}} = \frac{l \text{ (flagpole shadow)}}{l \text{ (pole shadow)}}$$

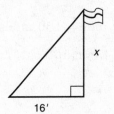

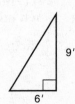

$$\frac{x}{9} = \frac{16}{6}$$

$$6x = 9 \times 16 = 144$$

$$x = \frac{144}{6} = 24$$

10. **2** 1 foot = 12 inches
9 feet 8 inches = 9 × 12 + 8
= 116 inches
116 ÷ 4 = 29 inches
29 ÷ 12 = 2 feet 5 inches

11. **1** The purse contains 6 + 5 + 8 = 19 coins.
    5 coins are dimes.

Probability =

$$\frac{\text{number of successful outcomes}}{\text{number of possible outcomes}}$$

    In this case, there are 5 successful outcomes since there are 5 dimes. And the number of possible outcomes is 19 since there are 19 coins in all.

    Thus, P = $\frac{5}{19}$.

12. **4** If we arrange the scores in order of magnitude the number in the middle is called the median.
    In this case, there are 9 scores. If we arrange them in order of magnitude the fifth score is the median. Notice that we will obtain the same result whether we arrange the scores from lowest to highest or from highest to lowest.
    Scores arranged from lowest to highest—

272, 274, 275, 276, 278, 281, 283, 284, 287
             ↓
        median

13. **5** The pens cost 3 for $.97.
    The cost of 1 dozen pens = 4($.97)
    = $3.88.
    The cost of 8 pencils = $4.60
    − 3.88 = $.72.
    The cost of 1 pencil = $.72 ÷ 8
    = 9 cents.

14. **1** 1 inch on the map = 150 miles

$3\frac{1}{2}$ inches on the map

$$= (3\frac{1}{2})(150)$$

$$= \frac{7}{2} \times 150 = 525 \text{ miles.}$$

15. **2** To find the perimeter of the figure we find the sum of the lengths of the four sides
2a + b + a + 3b + 3a + b + 3a + 2b
      = 9a + 7b.

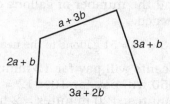

16. **4** The distance between point A and point B is 10 units. Thus, the midpoint of $\overline{AB}$ is located at 5 units to the right of point A.
    The coordinate of the midpoint of $\overline{AB}$ is 3.

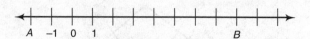

17. **5** 3 ties sold for $23
6 ties cost 2($23) = $46
3 shirts sold for $43
slacks sold for $32.75 per pair
2 pairs of slacks sold for
2($32.75) = $65.50
1 jacket sold for $58.45
$46 + $43 + $65.50 + $58.45
= $212.95

18. **3** If we write all the numbers as decimals, it is easier to arrange the numbers in order of size. 19% = .19,
$\frac{1}{2}$ = .50, $\frac{3}{5}$ = 60, and .080 may be
written as .08.
    The correct order from greatest to smallest is
    .80, .60, .50, .19, .08, or
    .8, $\frac{3}{5}$, $\frac{1}{2}$, 19%, .080

The correct choice is (3).

19. **3** Average speed = distance covered ÷ time of flight.
    Average speed = 1,364 miles ÷ $5\frac{1}{2}$ hours.

$$1,364 \div 5\frac{1}{2} = 1,364 \div \frac{11}{2}$$

$$= 1364 \times \frac{2}{11}$$

$1364 \div 11 = 124$, $124 \times 2 = 248$

20. **2** To write a number in scientific notation we write it as the product of a number between 1 and 10 and a power of 10. In this case, the number between 1 and 10 is 8.5. In going from 8.5 to 85,000,000,000 we move the decimal point 10 places to the right. Therefore $85,000,000,000 = 8.5 \times 10^{10}$.

21. **3** $3ab - x^2y = 3(4)(5) - (2)(2)(3)$
$$= 60 - 12 = 48$$

22. **3** The sum of the measures of the angles around the center of the circle is 360°. The fraction that represents the part of the total number of workers who are engaged in transportation is $\frac{20}{360}$.

$$\frac{20}{360} = \frac{1}{18}$$

$$\frac{1}{18} \text{ of } 180,000 = \frac{180,000}{18} = 10,000$$

23. **4** M = the number of persons in trade and finance

Let x = the number of persons in manufacturing

If 90° represents M

$$\frac{90}{M} = \frac{120}{x}$$

$$90x = 120M$$

$$x = \frac{120M}{90}$$

$$x = \frac{4M}{3} \text{ or } 4M \div 3$$

24. **4** Since $m\angle ABC = 68°$ and $\overline{BF}$ bisects $\angle ABC$ then $m\angle EBC = \frac{1}{2}(68) = 34°$.

Since $m\angle ACB = 72°$ and $\overline{CD}$ bisects $\angle ACB$ then $m\angle ECB = \frac{1}{2}(72) = 36°$.

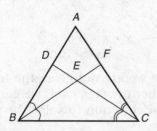

Since the sum of the measure of the angles of a triangle is 180°,

$$m\angle EBC + m\angle ECB + m\angle BEC = 180°$$
$$34 + 36 + m\angle BEC = 180°$$
$$70 + m\angle BEC = 180°$$
$$m\angle BEC = 180 - 70 = 110°$$

25. **3** Frank has $30.

Jack has $3 less, or $30 - $3 = $27.

Bill has $5 more than Jack, or Bill has $27 + $5 = $32.

26. **5** We know that John Davis lost at least 4 pounds each month. But he may have lost 4 pounds during one month, or even more. Not enough information is given to determine John Davis's exact weight after the 6-month period.

27. **2** To compute the annual interest on $10,000 at $8\frac{1}{2}$% we find $10,000 × .085 = $850.

Thus, every 6 months Mr. Ames receives $\frac{1}{2}$ of $850 = $425.

28. **5** 3 feet = $3 \times 12 = 36$ inches.

1 foot 10 inches = $12 + 10 = 22$ inches.

1 foot 2 inches = $12 + 2 = 14$ inches.

For the volume of the aquarium we use the formula $V = lwh$.

In this case, $l = 36$, $w = 22$, and $h = 14$.

$V = 36 \times 22 \times 14 = 11,088$ cubic inches.

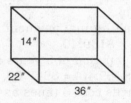

To find the number of gallons in the aquarium when it is full we divide 11,088 by 231.

$$11,088 \div 231 = 48$$

29. **3** Let $9x$ = the number of men at the meeting.

And $2x$ = the number of women at the meeting.

$$2x = 12$$
$$x = 6$$
$$9x = 9(6) = 54$$

30. **5** The slope of $\overleftrightarrow{AB}$

$$= \frac{\text{change in } y\text{-coordinates}}{\text{change in } x\text{-coordinates}}$$

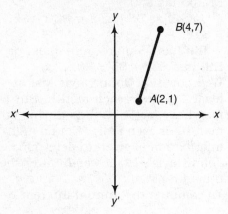

Slope of $\overleftrightarrow{AB} = \dfrac{7-1}{4-2} = \dfrac{6}{2} = 3$

31. **3** Let x = number of points scored by Jim.

And $3x$ = number of points scored by Bill.

$$x + 3x = 56$$
$$4x = 56$$
$$x = 56 \div 4 = 14$$
$$3x = 3(14) = 42$$

32. **4** According to the table Michael pays $4.69 per $1,000 quarterly, or 10($4.69) = $46.90 per quarter.

Michael's annual payments are 4($46.90) = $187.60.

33. **1** Philip pays $9.47 per $1,000 semi-annually, or 10($9.47) = $94.70 per half year.

Philip's annual payment is 2 × $94.70 = $189.40.

Over a period of 5 years Philip pays 5($189.40) = $947.00.

34. **1** Six pencils cost 6 times as much as one pencil. Since y is the cost of one pencil, the cost of 6 pencils is 6 times $y = 6y$.

35. **5** To find Mr. Martin's earnings we must multiply 42 by 12 and add this to the product of 37 and 12. From the choices we must select the equivalent of $42 \times 12 + 37 \times 12$.

$$42 \times 12 + 37 \times 12 = 12(42 + 79)$$

36. **4** Total enrollment = 360 + 300 + 280

+ 260 = 1,200

The part of the total enrollment representing the freshmen class is

$$\frac{360}{1,200} = \frac{36}{120}$$

$$\frac{36}{120} = .3$$

$$.3 = .30 = 30\%$$

37. **3** m∠BCD = m∠ABC since pairs of alternate interior angles of parallel lines have equal measures. Thus m∠BCD = 112°.

$$m\angle ECD = \frac{1}{2}\, m\angle BCD$$

$$= \frac{1}{2}(112°) = 56°$$

38. **2** 22 ft. 4 in. = 22(12) + 4 = 268 inches

268 ÷ 4 = 67 inches per drape

$$\frac{67}{12} = 5\frac{7}{12}$$

Each drape is 5 feet 7 inches in length.

39. **4** According to the graph the population in 1992 was midway between 25,000 and 30,000.

$$25,000 + 30,000 = 55,000$$
$$55,000 \div 2 = 27,500$$

40. **3** According to the graph the population in 1990 was 20,000 and in 1991 it was also 20,000.

There was no change in population between 1990 and 1991.

41. **4** We use the formula $V = lwh$ to represent the volume of the rectangular solid. The volume of the rectangular solid is

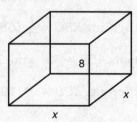

$$x \cdot x \cdot 8 = 8x^2$$
$$8x^2 = 392$$

42. **5** Since we are not given the total number of votes cast, we cannot set up an equation to solve the problem.

43. **2** If $AB = AC$, $m\angle C = m\angle B = 68°$.
Since $\overline{AD} \perp \overline{BC}$, $m\angle ADC = 90°$.

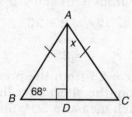

Since the sum of the measures of the angles of a triangle is 180°, we have
$68 + 90 + m\angle x = 180$
$158 + m\angle x = 180$
$m\angle x = 180 - 158 = 22°$

44. **4** In the right triangle we use the Pythagorean theorem to obtain

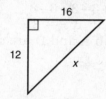

$x^2 = (12)^2 + (16)^2$
$x^2 = 144 + 256 = 400$
$x = \sqrt{400} = 20$

45. **3** Since $5^2 = 25$ and $6^2 = 36$, $\sqrt{30}$ is between 5 and 6.

46. **1** AD = radius of large circle = 20

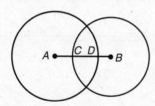

$CD = 6$
$AC = AD - CD = 20 - 6 = 14$
BC = radius of small circle = 8
$CD = 6$
$BD = BC - CD = 8 - 6 = 2$
$AB = AC + CD + DB = 14 + 6 + 2 = 22$

47. **4** $m\angle EBF = m\angle CBD = 50°$ since vertical angles have equal measures.

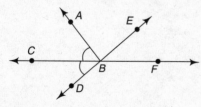

Since $\overleftrightarrow{CB}$ bisects $\angle ABD$, $m\angle ABC = m\angle CBD$.

Thus, $m\angle ABC = 50°$.

48. **4** To find the cost of n pounds of sugar at c cents per pound we multiply n by c to obtain nc.
To find the change received we subtract nc from 1.00, or 100 cents. The result is $100 - nc$.

49. **1** Let x = the number of students in the graduating class.
$.85x$ plan to go to college

$.85x = 170$
$x = \dfrac{170}{.85} = \dfrac{17000}{85} = 200$

50. **2** We divide the figure into two rectangles by drawing the dotted line.

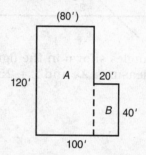

The width of rectangle $A = 100 - 20 = 80$
The length of rectangle $A = 120$
The area of rectangle $A = (80)(120) = 9600$ sq ft
The area of rectangle $B = 40 \times 20 = 800$ sq ft
Area of figure = $9600 + 800 = 10,400$ sq ft

51. **5** We check each inequality or equation in turn.
(1) $3(10) + 1 > 12$, $30 + 1 > 12$. True
(2) $2(10) - 3 < 25$, $20 - 3 < 25$. True
(3) $10^2 + 1 > 10^2 - 1$, $100 + 1 > 100 - 1$. True
(4) $4(10) - 1 = 39$, $40 - 1 = 39$. True
(5) $2(10) - 7 > 7 - 2(10)$, $20 - 7 < 7 - 20$. Not true
The correct choice is (5).

52. **5** Let x = measure of smaller acute angle.
And $4x$ = measure of larger acute angle.

$$x + 4x = 90$$
$$5x = 90$$
$$x = 90 \div 5 = 18$$
$$4x = 4(18) = 72°$$

53.4 The borrower pays 50 cents for the first three days plus 15 cents for each day after the third day. That is, $15(n - 3)$.

Thus, the correct formula is $C = 50 + 15(n - 3)$.

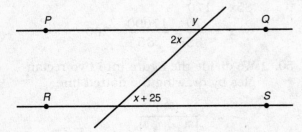

54.3 The angles shown in the figure having measures $2x$ and $x + 25$ are al-

ternate interior angles, so they are equal. To solve the equation, subtract x from both sides:

$$2x = x + 25$$
$$-x \quad -x$$
$$x = 25$$

55.1 Since $x = 25$ from the previous question, the alternative interior angles each measure 50°. Since y is supplementary to this angle, its measure is $180° - 50° = 130°$.

56.4
$$x^2 - x - 12 = 0$$
$$(x - 4)(x + 3) = 0$$
$$x - 4 = 0$$
$$x - 4 + 4 = 0 + 4$$
$$x = 4$$

or

$$x + 3 = 0$$
$$x + 3 - 3 = 0 - 3$$
$$x = -3$$

So both A and D are correct.

Answer Sheet for Practice Test Three

TEST 5: MATHEMATICS

1. ① ② ③ ④ ⑤
2. ① ② ③ ④ ⑤
3. ① ② ③ ④ ⑤
4. ① ② ③ ④ ⑤
5. ① ② ③ ④ ⑤
6. ① ② ③ ④ ⑤
7. ① ② ③ ④ ⑤
8. ① ② ③ ④ ⑤
9. ① ② ③ ④ ⑤
10. ① ② ③ ④ ⑤
11. ① ② ③ ④ ⑤
12. ① ② ③ ④ ⑤
13. ① ② ③ ④ ⑤
14. ① ② ③ ④ ⑤
15. ① ② ③ ④ ⑤
16. ① ② ③ ④ ⑤
17. ① ② ③ ④ ⑤
18. ① ② ③ ④ ⑤
19. ① ② ③ ④ ⑤

20. ① ② ③ ④ ⑤
21. ① ② ③ ④ ⑤
22. ① ② ③ ④ ⑤
23. ① ② ③ ④ ⑤
24. ① ② ③ ④ ⑤
25. ① ② ③ ④ ⑤
26. ① ② ③ ④ ⑤
27. ① ② ③ ④ ⑤
28. ① ② ③ ④ ⑤
29. ① ② ③ ④ ⑤
30. ① ② ③ ④ ⑤
31. ① ② ③ ④ ⑤
32. ① ② ③ ④ ⑤
33. ① ② ③ ④ ⑤
34. ① ② ③ ④ ⑤
35. ① ② ③ ④ ⑤
36. ① ② ③ ④ ⑤
37. ① ② ③ ④ ⑤
38. ① ② ③ ④ ⑤

39. ① ② ③ ④ ⑤
40. ① ② ③ ④ ⑤
41. ① ② ③ ④ ⑤
42. ① ② ③ ④ ⑤
43. ① ② ③ ④ ⑤
44. ① ② ③ ④ ⑤
45. ① ② ③ ④ ⑤
46. ① ② ③ ④ ⑤
47. ① ② ③ ④ ⑤
48. ① ② ③ ④ ⑤
49. ① ② ③ ④ ⑤
50. ① ② ③ ④ ⑤
51. ① ② ③ ④ ⑤
52. ① ② ③ ④ ⑤
53. ① ② ③ ④ ⑤
54. ① ② ③ ④ ⑤
55. ① ② ③ ④ ⑤
56. ① ② ③ ④ ⑤

TEST 5: MATHEMATICS

Tests of General Educational Development
Directions*

The Mathematics Test consists of multiple-choice questions intended to measure general mathematics skills and problem-solving ability. The questions are based on short readings that often include a graph, chart, or figure.

You will have 90 minutes to complete the questions in this test. Work carefully, but do not spend too much time on any one question. Be sure you answer every question. You will not be penalized for incorrect answers.

Formulas you may need are given on page 156. Only some of the questions will require you to use a formula. Not all the formulas given will be needed.

Some questions contain more information than you will need to solve the problem; other questions do not give enough information. If the question does not give enough information to solve the problem, the correct answer choice is "Not enough information is given."

The use of calculators is not allowed.

Do not write in the test booklet. The test administrator will give you blank paper for your calculations. Record your answers on the separate answer sheet provided. Be sure all information is properly recorded on the answer sheet.

To record your answers, fill in the numbered circle on the answer sheet that corresponds to the answer you select for each question in the test booklet.

FOR EXAMPLE:

If a grocery bill totaling $15.75 is paid with a $20.00 bill, how much change should be returned?

(1) $5.26
(2) $4.75
(3) $4.25
(4) $3.75
(5) $3.25

(On Answer Sheet)

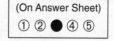

The correct answer is "$4.25"; therefore, answer space 3 would be marked on the answer sheet.

Do not rest the point of your pencil on the answer sheet while you are considering your answer. Make no stray or unnecessary marks. If you change an answer, erase your first mark completely. Mark only <u>one</u> answer space for each question; multiple answers will be scored as incorrect. Do not fold or crease your answer sheet. All test materials must be returned to the test administrator.

DO NOT BEGIN TAKING THE TEST UNTIL TOLD TO DO SO

* Reprinted with permission of the American Council on Education.

TEST 5: MATHEMATICS

FORMULAS*

Description	Formula
AREA (*A*) of a:	
square	$A = s^2$; where s = side
rectangle	$A = \ell w$; where ℓ = length, w = width
parallelogram	$A = bh$; where b = base, h = height
triangle	$A = \dfrac{1}{2}\, bh$; where b = base, h = height
circle	$A = \pi r^2$; where r = radius and π is approximately equal to 3.14
PERIMETER (*P*) of a:	
square	$P = 4s$; where s = side
rectangle	$P = 2\ell + 2w$; where ℓ = length, w = width
triangle	$P = a + b + c$; where a, b, and c are the sides
circumference (*C*) of a circle	$C = \pi d$; where d = diameter and π is approximately equal to 3.14
VOLUME (*V*) of a:	
cube	$V = s^3$; where s = side
rectangular container	$V = \ell wh$; where ℓ = length, w = width, h = height
cylinder	$V = \pi r^2 h$; where r = radius, h = height, and π is approximately equal to 3.14
Pythagorean relationship	$c^2 = a^2 + b^2$; where c = hypotenuse, a and b are legs of a right triangle
distance (*d*) between two points in a plane	$d = \sqrt{(x_2 - x_1)^2 + (y_2 - y_1)^2}$; where (x_1, y_1) and (x_2, y_2) are two points in a plane
slope (*m*) of a line	$m = \dfrac{y_2 - y_1}{x_2 - x_1}$; where (x_1, y_1) and (x_2, y_2) are two points on the line
mean	$mean = \dfrac{x_1 + x_2 + \cdots + x_n}{n}$; where the x's are the values for which a mean is desired, and n = number of values for x
median	The *median* is the middle value of an odd number of ordered scores, and halfway between the two middle values of an even number of ordered scores.
simple interest (*i*)	$i = prt$; where p = principal, r = rate, t = time
distance (*d*) as function of rate and time	$d = rt$; where r = rate, t = time
total cost (*c*)	$c = nr$; where n = number of units, r = cost per unit

* Reprinted with permission of the American Council on Education.

TEST 5: MATHEMATICS

<u>Directions:</u> Choose the <u>one best answer</u> to each question.

1. Luisa worked 40 hours and earned $6.30 per hour. Her friend Joan earned $8.40 per hour at her job. How many hours did Joan have to work in order to equal Luisa's earnings for 40 hours?

   (1) 252
   (2) 20
   (3) 30
   (4) 25
   (5) Not enough information is given.

2. In the figure below, $\triangle ABC$ is a right triangle and $\overline{CD} \perp \overline{AB}$. If the measure of $\angle CAD = 40°$, what is the measure of $\angle DCB$?

   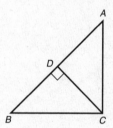

   (1) 10°
   (2) 20°
   (3) 40°
   (4) 50°
   (5) 90°

3. The number of students in a class is x. One day 5 students were absent. What fractional part of the class was present?

   (1) $\dfrac{x}{5}$

   (2) $\dfrac{5}{x}$

   (3) $\dfrac{5}{x-5}$

   (4) $\dfrac{x+5}{5}$

   (5) $\dfrac{x-5}{x}$

4. The gasoline gauge shows that a gasoline tank is $\dfrac{1}{3}$ full. In order to fill the tank, 16 gallons of gasoline are added. How many gallons of gasoline does the tank hold when full?

   (1) 20
   (2) 24
   (3) 30
   (4) 32
   (5) 48

5. What is the length of the ramp in feet in the figure below?

   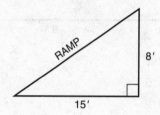

   (1) 15
   (2) 16
   (3) 17
   (4) 19
   (5) Not enough information is given.

6. At a luncheon, 48 half-pints of fruit juice are served. What is the cost of these servings at $3.50 per gallon of fruit juice?

   (1) $6.00
   (2) $7.00
   (3) $10.50
   (4) $12.50
   (5) $15.00

GO ON TO THE NEXT PAGE

TEST 5: MATHEMATICS

7. If $5x - 1 = 34$, then $2\frac{1}{2}x$ is equal to

   (1) 7

   (2) 14

   (3) $16\frac{2}{3}$

   (4) 17

   (5) $17\frac{1}{2}$

8. On the line segment below, if $AC = 18$ inches and $BC = 8$ inches, then the ratio $AB:BC$ is equal to

   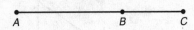

   A   B   C

   (1) 2:1

   (2) 4:5

   (3) 3:2

   (4) 5:4

   (5) Not enough information is given.

9. A rectangular living room has a floor area of 322 square feet. If the length of the room is 23 feet, how many feet are there in the perimeter of the room?

   (1) 28

   (2) 37

   (3) 45

   (4) 60

   (5) 74

10. Don Brown priced a TV set at $280 at the Triangle Store. He then saw an advertisement for the same TV set at the ABC Store announcing 20% off on all merchandise. What additional information does Don need in order to make a wise buying decision?

    (1) The Triangle Store has a better reputation than the ABC Store.

    (2) The sales tax on TV purchases is 5%.

    (3) Both stores have a $5 delivery charge.

    (4) The name of the manufacturer of the TV set.

    (5) The price from which the ABC Store deducts 20%.

11. A crew can load a truck in 3 hours. What part of the truck can they load in 45 minutes?

    (1) $\frac{1}{8}$

    (2) $\frac{1}{4}$

    (3) $\frac{1}{3}$

    (4) $\frac{1}{2}$

    (5) Not enough information is given.

12. Given the equation $x^2 + x - 6 = 0$, which of the following choices give(s) a complete solution of the equation?

    A. 2
    B. −2
    C. 3
    D. −3

    (1) A only

    (2) A and D

    (3) B and C

    (4) A and C

    (5) C and D

GO ON TO THE NEXT PAGE

TEST 5: MATHEMATICS

13. What is the perimeter of the figure below?

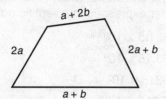

(1) $6a + b$

(2) $5a + 5b$

(3) $6a + 4b$

(4) $4a + 4b$

(5) $3a + 5b$

14. Henry has $5 more than Bob. If Henry's money is added to twice Bob's money the sum will be $65. How much money did Bob have?

(1) $10

(2) $12

(3) $15

(4) $20

(5) Not enough information is given.

15. A motel charges $48.00 per day for a double room. In addition, there is a 5% tax. How much does a couple pay for several days' stay?

(1) $144.00

(2) $151.20

(3) $156.20

(4) $158.40

(5) Not enough information is given.

16. If the square of a number is added to the number increased by 4, the result is 60. If n represents the number, which equation can be used to find n?

(1) $n^2 + 4 = 60$

(2) $n^2 + 4n = 60$

(3) $n^2 + n + 4 = 60$

(4) $n^2 + 60 = 4n + 4$

(5) $n^2 + n = 64$

17. A box of cereal is priced at x cents per box. A customer has a 15 cents off coupon. If the store reduces prices by doubling the value of each coupon, how much does the customer pay for the box of cereal, in cents?

(1) $x - 15$

(2) $x - 30$

(3) $x + 15$

(4) $x + 30$

(5) Not enough information is given.

18. The measures of the angles of a triangle are in the ratio $3 : 2 : 1$. What is the measure of the largest angle of the triangle?

(1) $65°$

(2) $70°$

(3) $72°$

(4) $80°$

(5) $90°$

GO ON TO THE NEXT PAGE

TEST 5: MATHEMATICS

19. In the figure shown below, if m ∠1 = 36°
and m ∠2 = 2 (m ∠3), then m ∠3 equals

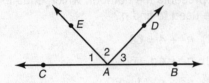

  (1) 36°
  (2) 40°
  (3) 44°
  (4) 48°
  (5) Not enough information is given.

20. Mrs. Adams bought 4 pounds of beef and
$3\frac{1}{2}$ pounds of chicken for $13.98. If the
beef cost $2.76 per pound, what was
the cost of chicken per pound?

  (1) $.72
  (2) $.80
  (3) $.84
  (4) $.87
  (5) $.92

21. A carpenter earns $16 per hour and his
assistant earns half as much. Which of the
following expressions represent how many
dollars both men earned on a job that took
9 hours?

  (1) $9(16) + 9(\frac{1}{2})$

  (2) $9(16) + 9(10)$
  (3) $16(8) + 9(9)$

  (4) $16(\frac{1}{2}) + 9(\frac{1}{2})$

  (5) $9(16) + 9(8)$

22. The distance between two heavenly bodies
is 63,150,000,000 miles. What is this
number expressed in scientific notation?

  (1) 631.5×10^8
  (2) 63.15×10^9
  (3) 6315×10^7
  (4) 6.315×10^{10}
  (5) 6.315×10^{-10}

23. An English class has an enrollment of 14
boys and 12 girls. On a rainy day 4 boys
and 3 girls are absent. If a student is called
at random to recite, what is the probability
that the student called is a girl?

  (1) $\frac{9}{19}$

  (2) $\frac{10}{19}$

  (3) $\frac{12}{26}$

  (4) $\frac{9}{14}$

  (5) Not enough information is given.

24. Mr. Barnes has invested $12,000 in bonds
that pay interest at the rate of 9% annually.
What is Mr. Barnes's annual income from
this investment?

  (1) $108
  (2) $180
  (3) $1,080
  (4) $10,800
  (5) $12,000

25. For which value of x is the inequality $3x + 2 < 14$ true?

  (1) 3
  (2) 4
  (3) 5
  (4) 6
  (5) 7

GO ON TO THE NEXT PAGE

TEST 5: MATHEMATICS

26. The graph below shows what happened to each $100 taken in by a small business firm. How many dollars out of each $100 taken in represented profit?

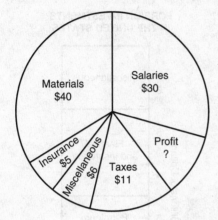

(1) $5

(2) $6

(3) $7

(4) $7.5

(5) $8

27. Over a period of 5 months John saved $659. At the same rate of saving, which expression below represents what he saved over a period of 9 months? Let *y* represent savings for 9 months.

(1) $y = 9(659)$

(2) $y = \dfrac{5(659)}{9}$

(3) $y = 5(659)$

(4) $y = \dfrac{9(659)}{5}$

(5) $y = 5(9)(659)$

28. Ben scored 7 more points than Jack in a basketball game. Paul scored 2 points less than Jack in the same game. If the three boys scored a total of 38 points, how many points did Jack score?

(1) 5

(2) 9

(3) 11

(4) 14

(5) 15

29. A box in the form of a rectangular solid has a square base 5 feet in length and a height of *h* feet. If the volume of the rectangular solid is 200 cubic feet, which of the following equations may be used to find *h*?

(1) $5h = 200$

(2) $5h^2 = 200$

(3) $25h = 200$

(4) $h = 200 \div 5$

(5) $h = 5(200)$

30. Which point on the number line below represents the closest approximation to the square root of 12?

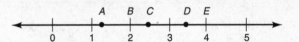

(1) *A*

(2) *B*

(3) *C*

(4) *D*

(5) *E*

GO ON TO THE NEXT PAGE

TEST 5: MATHEMATICS

31. The diagram below represents a large living room. What is the area of the room in square yards?

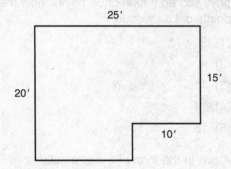

25'

20'

15'

10'

   (1) 16.6
   (2) 33.3
   (3) 45
   (4) 50
   (5) 450

32. If one plane can carry x passengers, how many planes will be needed to carry y passengers?

   (1) xy

   (2) $\dfrac{x}{y}$

   (3) $\dfrac{y}{x}$

   (4) $\dfrac{1}{xy}$

   (5) $x + y$

33. As shown on the graph below, by what amount does the investment in manufacturing exceed the amount invested in petroleum?

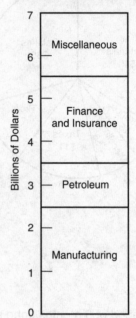

**FOREIGN INVESTMENTS
IN THE UNITED STATES**

Billions of Dollars

Miscellaneous

Finance and Insurance

Petroleum

Manufacturing

   (1) 1\frac{1}{2}$ million

   (2) 3\frac{1}{2}$ million

   (3) $0.5 billion

   (4) 1\frac{1}{2}$ billion

   (5) 3\frac{1}{2}$ billion

GO ON TO THE NEXT PAGE

TEST 5: MATHEMATICS

34. If the point $(x,3)$ is on the graph of the equation $x + y = 7$, what is the value of x?

    (1) 4
    (2) 3
    (3) 7
    (4) 1
    (5) 0

35. On a road map, $\frac{1}{4}$ inch represents 8 miles of actual road distance. The towns of Alton and Waverly are represented by points $2\frac{1}{8}$ inches apart on the map. What is the actual distance, in miles, between Alton and Waverly?

    (1) 17
    (2) 32
    (3) 40
    (4) 60
    (5) 68

36. At a certain time of day, a man 6 feet tall casts a shadow 4 feet in length. At the same time, a church steeple casts a shadow 28 feet in length. How high, in feet, is the church steeple?

    (1) 30
    (2) 32
    (3) 42
    (4) 48
    (5) 56

37. A dealer sells books at 40% above cost. How much does the dealer pay for a shipment of 6 dozen books that he sells for $7 per book?

    (1) $360
    (2) $380
    (3) $450
    (4) $504
    (5) $520

38. In the figure below, $\overleftrightarrow{AB}$ and $\overleftrightarrow{CD}$ are both parallel to the x-axis. The coordinates of B are $(5,4)$ and the coordinates of D are $(5,-3)$. The perpendicular distance between $\overleftrightarrow{AB}$ and $\overleftrightarrow{CD}$ is

    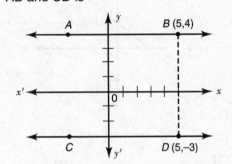

    (1) −2
    (2) 5
    (3) 6
    (4) 7
    (5) 10

39. Evaluate $(6 \times 10^5) \div (4 \times 10^3)$.

    (1) 20
    (2) 100
    (3) 150
    (4) 1,500
    (5) 2,000

GO ON TO THE NEXT PAGE

TEST 5: MATHEMATICS

40. In the diagram below, if the slope of $\overleftrightarrow{AB}$ is 1, what is the value of y?

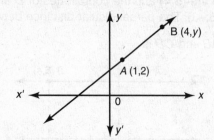

    (1) 1
    (2) 2
    (3) 3
    (4) 4
    (5) 5

Questions 41 through 43 are based on the following information.

The bar graph below shows the number of gallons of paint sold by a local hardware store in one week.

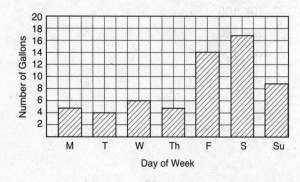

41. How much paint was sold on Wednesday?

    (1) 3 gallons
    (2) 4 gallons
    (3) 5 gallons
    (4) 6 gallons
    (5) 7 gallons

42. How much more paint was sold on Saturday than on Monday?

    (1) 6 gallons
    (2) 8 gallons
    (3) 10 gallons
    (4) 11 gallons
    (5) 12 gallons

43. What was the total amount of paint sold by the store that week?

    (1) 20 gallons
    (2) 25 gallons
    (3) 30 gallons
    (4) 60 gallons
    (5) Not enough information is given.

44. O is the center of the circle below and the measure of $\angle O$ is 70°. What is the measure of $\angle OAB$?

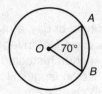

    (1) 55°
    (2) 60°
    (3) 65°
    (4) 70°
    (5) 75°

GO ON TO THE NEXT PAGE

TEST 5: MATHEMATICS

45. Sylvia took an automobile trip. The table below shows the mileage she covered during one afternoon. If she drove at a steady rate, how many miles had she covered at 4:15 P.M.?

TIME	3:00 P.M.	4:00 P.M.	5:00 P.M.
Distance covered in miles	80	124	168

   (1) 30

   (2) 132

   (3) 135

   (4) 140

   (5) Not enough information is given.

46. The following is a list of ingredients used in making cornmeal crisps:

   1 cup yellow cornmeal

   $\frac{1}{2}$ cup of sifted flour

   $\frac{2}{3}$ teaspoon salt

   $\frac{1}{4}$ teaspoon baking powder

   2 tablespoons melted shortening

   $\frac{1}{3}$ cup of milk

If Joan finds that she cannot accurately measure $\frac{1}{3}$ cup of milk and decides to use a full cup of milk, then she will have to use

   (1) 1 cup of sifted flour

   (2) 2 teaspoons of salt

   (3) 3 teaspoons of baking powder

   (4) 3 tablespoons of melted shortening

   (5) $2\frac{1}{2}$ cups of yellow cornmeal

47. According to the graph below, what was the number of shirts produced in 1980?

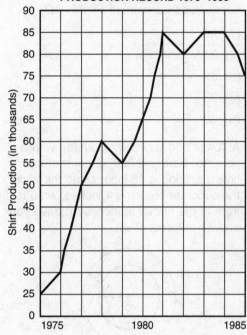

SHARPEE SHIRT MANUFACTURING CO. PRODUCTION RECORD 1975–1985

   (1) 2,500

   (2) 6,500

   (3) 25,000

   (4) 65,000

   (5) 70,000

48. A house and a lot cost $120,000. If the house cost three times as much as the lot, how much did the house cost?

   (1) $30,000

   (2) $40,000

   (3) $60,000

   (4) $90,000

   (5) $100,000

GO ON TO THE NEXT PAGE

TEST 5: MATHEMATICS

49. A bookcase has 3 large shelves and 4 small shelves. Each large shelf contains 8 more books than each small shelf. If the bookcase contains 297 books, how many books does each small shelf hold?

    (1) 29
    (2) 31
    (3) 32
    (4) 35
    (5) 39

50. A flower bed is circular in shape with a concrete border. If the diameter of the flower section is 40 inches and the width of the concrete border is 4 inches, what is the area of the border in inches? (Leave your answer in terms of π.)

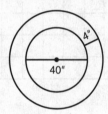

    (1) 16π
    (2) 176π
    (3) 180π
    (4) 200π
    (5) 240π

51. Mrs. Edwards buys 40 feet of woolen material. She wishes to use this material for scarfs. How many scarfs 3 feet 4 inches in length can she cut from this material?

    (1) 12
    (2) 15
    (3) 16
    (4) 18
    (5) 120

52. A food packager has to decide how to pack boxes of cereal. He has the following package sizes to consider, based upon weight:

    A. 18.5 ounces, 1 pound, 7.95 ounces, $\frac{1}{2}$ pound, 20 ounces

    B. 20 ounces, 18.5 ounces, 1 pound, $\frac{1}{2}$ pound, 7.95 ounces

    C. 1 pound, 20 ounces, 18.5 ounces, 7.95 ounces, $\frac{1}{2}$ pound

    D. 20 ounces, 18.5 ounces, 7.95 ounces, 1 pound, $\frac{1}{2}$ pound

    E. 7.95 ounces, 1 pound, 20 ounces, $\frac{1}{2}$ pound, 18.5 ounces

    Which one of the above is arranged in order from the heaviest to the lightest?

    (1) A
    (2) B
    (3) C
    (4) D
    (5) E

53. If $\overleftrightarrow{AB}$ is parallel to $\overleftrightarrow{CD}$ in the diagram below, the angles in each of the following pairs are congruent EXCEPT

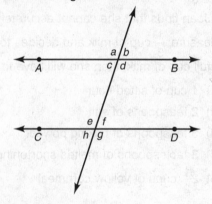

    (1) ∠a ≅ ∠d
    (2) ∠b ≅ ∠f
    (3) ∠c ≅ ∠b
    (4) ∠f ≅ ∠c
    (5) ∠b ≅ ∠g

GO ON TO THE NEXT PAGE

TEST 5: MATHEMATICS

54. $A + B + C = 180$. If $A = B$ and $B = 2C$, then the value of C is

    (1) 36
    (2) 45
    (3) 60
    (4) 72
    (5) 90

55. Mrs. Evans buys 2 pounds 6 ounces of apples at $.72 per pound and 3 pounds 4 ounces of peaches at $.56 per pound. How much change does she receive from a $5 bill?

    (1) $1.35
    (2) $1.47
    (3) $1.82
    (4) $3.53
    (5) Not enough information is given.

56. A dealer buys ties that are priced at 6 for $39. How much does a shipment of 15 dozen ties cost?

    (1) $234
    (2) $585
    (3) $785
    (4) $1,070
    (5) $1,170

END OF EXAMINATION

Answer Key

1. 3	11. 2	21. 5	31. 4	41. 4	51. 1
2. 3	12. 2	22. 4	32. 3	42. 5	52. 2
3. 5	13. 3	23. 1	33. 4	43. 4	53. 5
4. 2	14. 4	24. 3	34. 1	44. 1	54. 1
5. 3	15. 5	25. 1	35. 5	45. 3	55. 2
6. 3	16. 3	26. 5	36. 3	46. 2	56. 5
7. 5	17. 2	27. 4	37. 1	47. 4	
8. 4	18. 5	28. 3	38. 4	48. 4	
9. 5	19. 4	29. 3	39. 3	49. 5	
10. 5	20. 3	30. 4	40. 5	50. 2	

Self-Analysis

WHAT'S YOUR SCORE?

_____right _____wrong

Excellent	51–56
Good	44–50
Fair	38–43

If your score was low, the explanation of the correct answers that follows will help you. You may obtain additional help by reviewing the self-analysis chart that follows.

Did you get at least 38 correct answers? If not, you need more practice for the Mathematics Test. You can improve your performance to Good or Excellent by analyzing your errors. To determine the areas in which you need further study, review the chart that follows. The question numbers from Practice Test Three appear in the column to the left. Circle the questions you answered incorrectly. (Unsolved problems are counted as incorrect.) Refer to the Chapter and Chapter Section indicated for each question for additional review.

SELF-ANALYSIS CHART

Question	Chapter	Chapter Section	Question	Chapter	Chapter Section
1	3	Types of problems	29	6	Volume
2	6	Shapes	30	4	Exponents
3	4	Translation	31	6	Shapes
4	4	Translation	32	4	Translation
		Solving equations	33	7	Tables
5	6	Pythagorean	34	4	Solving equations
		relationship	35	3	Types of problems
6	5	Liquid measurement	36	6	Shapes
7	4	Solving equations	37	4	Percent
8	4	Proportion		3	Types of problems
9	6	Shapes	38	6	Coordinates
10	3	How to read a		4	Formulas
		math problem	39	4	Order of operations
11	4	Proportion			Exponents
	3	Types of problems	40	4	Formulas
12	4	Factoring	41	7	Graphs
13	6	Shapes	42	7	Graphs
14	4	Translation	43	7	Graphs
		Solving equations	44	6	Shapes
15	4	Percent	45	4	Proportion
16	4	Translation	46	3	Types of problems
17	4	Translation	47	7	Graphs
18	4	Proportion	48	4	Translation
	6	Shapes			Solving equations
19	6	Lines and angles	49	4	Translation
20	3	Types of problems			Inequalities
21	4	Translation	50	6	Shapes
22	4	Scientific notation	51	5	Linear measurement
23	7	Analyzing data	52	3	Sequencing
24	4	Formulas	53	6	Lines and angles
25	4	Inequalities	54	4	Solving equations
26	7	Graphs	55	5	Weight measurement
27	4	Translation	56	5	Conversion factors
28	4	Translation		3	Types of problems
		Solving equations			

Answers Explained

1. **3** Luisa earned a total of 40($6.30) = $252. To find the number of hours it would take Joan to earn $252, we must divide $252 by $8.40.
$252.00 \div 8.40 = 30$ hours

2. **3** Since $m\angle ACB = 90°$ and $m\angle CAD = 40°$ then $m\angle B = 180° - 90° - 40° = 50°$. In $\triangle BCD$, $m\angle CDB = 90°$ and $m\angle B = 50°$.
Therefore,
$m\angle DCB = 180° - 90° - 50° = 40°$.

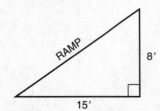

3. **5** If the class has x students and 5 students are absent then $x - 5$ students are present.

$$\frac{x-5}{x} = \frac{\text{number of students present}}{\text{number of students in class}}$$

4. **2** If the gauge shows $\frac{1}{3}$ full, then the tank is $\frac{2}{3}$ empty.

$\frac{2}{3}$ of the tank = 16 gallons

$\frac{1}{3}$ of the tank = $\frac{1}{2}(16) = 8$ gallons

$\frac{3}{3}$ of the tank = $3(8) = 24$ gallons

5. **3** Let x = length of ramp.
We use the Pythagorean theorem to obtain the equation
$x^2 = 8^2 + 15^2$
$x^2 = 64 + 225 = 289$
$x = \sqrt{289} = 17$

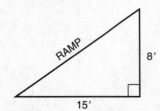

6. **3** 48 half-pints = 24 pints
Since 2 pints = 1 quart,
24 pints = 12 quarts.
Since 4 quarts = 1 gallon,
12 quarts = 3 gallons.

$3($3.50$) = 10.50

7. **5** $5x - 1 = 34$
$5x = 34 + 1 = 35$
$x = 35 \div 5 = 7$
$2\frac{1}{2}x = \frac{5x}{2} = \frac{5}{2} \times 7 = \frac{35}{2}$, or $17\frac{1}{2}$

8. **4** If $AC = 18$ and $BC = 8$ then $AB = 18 - 8 = 10$.
The ratio $AB:BC = 10:8$, or $5:4$.

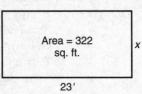

9. **5** Let x = width of room.
$23x = 322$
$x = 332 \div 23 = 14$
Perimeter =
$23 + 14 + 23 + 14 = 74$ feet

Area = 322 sq. ft. x

23'

10. **5** In order to determine the price that the ABC Store charges for the TV set, Don must know the price from which the store deducts 20%.

11. **2** If a crew can load a truck in 3 hours, then it can load $\frac{1}{3}$ of the truck in 1 hour.

In 45 minutes, or $\frac{3}{4}$ of an hour, the crew can load $\frac{3}{4} \times \frac{1}{3} = \frac{1}{4}$ of the truck.

12. **2** $x^2 + x - 6 = 0$
$(x + 3)(x - 2) = 0$
$\quad x + 3 = 0$
$\quad x + 3 - 3 = 0 - 3$
$\quad\quad\quad x = -3$
or
$\quad\quad x - 2 = 0$
$\quad x - 2 + 2 = 0 + 2$
$\quad\quad\quad x = 2$
The correct choice is (2).

13. **3** To find the perimeter of the figure we must find the sum of the lengths of its sides.
$2a + a + b + 2a + b + a + 2b$
$= 6a + 4b$

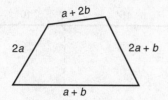

14. **4** Let x = Bob's money.
And $x + 5$ = Henry's money.
$x + 5 + 2x = 65$
$3x + 5 = 65$
$3x = 65 - 5 = 60$
$x = 60 \div 3 = \$20$

15. **5** We cannot compute the cost unless we are told the number of days that the couple stays at the motel. This information is not given.

16. **3** Let n = the number.
Then n^2 = the square of the number.
And $n + 4 =$
the number increased by 4.
The equation is $n^2 + n + 4 = 60$.

17. **2** Because the coupon has double value, the reduction in price is $2(15¢) = 30$ cents.
The cost of the cereal is $x - 30$.

18. **5** Let $3x$ = the measure of the largest angle.
And $2x$ = the measure of the second angle.
And x = the measure of the third angle.
$3x + 2x + x = 180$
$6x = 180$
$x = 180 \div 6 = 30$
$3x = 3(30) = 90°$

19. **4** Let $x = m\angle 3$.
And $2x = m\angle 2$.
$m\angle 1 + m\angle 2 + m\angle 3 = 180°$
$36 + 2x + x = 180$
$3x + 36 = 180$
$3x = 180 - 36 = 144$
$x = 144 \div 3 = 48°$

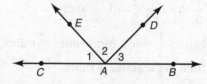

20. **3** The beef costs $4(\$2.76) = \$11.04$.
The chicken cost $\$13.98 - \$11.04 = \$2.94$.
To find the cost of chicken per pound, we divide $\$2.94$ by $3\frac{1}{2}$, or by $\frac{7}{2}$.

$2.94 \div \frac{7}{2} = 2.94 \times \frac{2}{7} = .84$

The cost of the chicken was $.84 per pound.

21. **5** The carpenter earns $16 per hour or 9(16) dollars for 9 hours of work.
The assistant earns $8 per hour of 9(8) for 9 hours of work.
The two men together earned 9(16) + 9(8) dollars.

22. **4** To express a number in scientific notation we express it as the product of a number between 1 and 10 and a power of 10. In this case, the number between 1 and 10 is 6.315. In going from 6.315 to 63,150,000,000 we move the decimal point 10 places to the right. Each such move represents a multiplication by 10. Thus, the entire movement of the decimal point represents multiplication by 10^{10}.
Thus, $63,150,000,000 = 6.315 \times 10^{10}$

23. **1** Probability =
$\dfrac{\text{number of successful outcomes}}{\text{total number of outcomes}}$
In this case, there are 9 girls who could have been called upon.
The total number of students who could have been called upon was 19.
Probability = $\dfrac{9}{19}$

24. **3** $\$12,000 \times .09 = \$1,080$

25. **1** $3x + 2 < 14$
$3x < 14 - 2$
$3x < 12$
$x < 4$
The only choice less than 4 is answer (1) 3.
Thus, the substitution of 3 for x satisfies the inequality. Note that the substitution of any of the other values given for x would make the statement of the inequality untrue.

26. **5** If we add the amounts given
$11 + 6 + 5 + 40 + 30 = \$92$
This leaves $8 for profit.

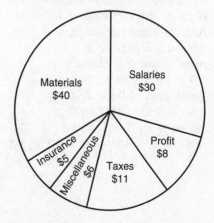

27.**4** We set up the proportion
$$\frac{5}{659} = \frac{9}{y}$$
$$5y = 9(659)$$
$$y = \frac{9(659)}{5}$$

28.**3** Let x = the number of points scored by Jack.
And $x + 7$ = the number of points scored by Ben.
And $x - 2$ = the number of points scored by Paul.
$$x + x + 7 + x - 2 = 38$$
$$3x + 5 = 38$$
$$3x = 38 - 5 = 33$$
$$x = 33 \div 3 = 11$$

29.**3** We use the formula $V = lwh$
In this case, $l = 5$, $w = 5$, and $h = h$.
Therefore, $V = 5 \times 5 \times h$
$V = 25h$
And $25h = 200$

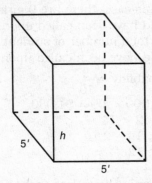

30.**4** $\sqrt{12} = 3.46$, or 3.5 to the nearest tenth
Point D is paired with 3.5 on the number line.

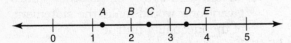

31.**4** Divide the floor space into 2 rectangles by drawing the line segment NM.
Area of the rectangle = lw
Area of large rectangle =
$20 \times 15 = 300$ sq ft
Area of small rectangle =
$10 \times 15 = 150$ sq ft
Total area of floor space =
$150 + 300 = 450$ sq ft
Since 9 sq ft = 1 sq yd,
450 sq ft = $450 \div 9 = 50$ sq yd

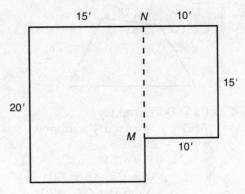

32.**3** We may develop a method of solving this problem by replacing the letters by numbers. For example,
If one plane can carry 200 passengers, how many planes will be needed to carry 1,000 passengers?
The answer to this problem is obtained by dividing 1,000 by 200.
Similarly, the answer to the original problem is $\frac{y}{x}$.

33.**4** Foreign investment in manufacturing = $\$2\frac{1}{2}$ billion

Foreign investment in petroleum = $1 billion

Difference = $\$1\frac{1}{2}$ billion

34.**1** The equation $x + y = 7$ states that the sum of two numbers is 7. Since the value of y is 3, then $x + 3 = 7$ and $x = 7 - 3$, or 4.

35.**5** $\frac{1}{4}$ inch represents 8 miles.

$\frac{4}{4}$, or 1 inch, represents $4 \times 8 = 32$ miles

2 inches represents $2 \times 32 = 64$ miles
$\frac{1}{8}$ inch = $\frac{1}{2}$ of $\frac{1}{4}$ inch

Since $\frac{1}{4}$ inch represents 8 miles, $\frac{1}{8}$ inch represents 4 miles.

$2\frac{1}{8}$ inches represent $64 + 4 = 68$ miles

36.**3** Since the triangles shown are similar, the measures of their corresponding sides are in proportion. That is,

$$\frac{x\,(\text{height of steeple})}{6\,(\text{height of man})} =$$

$$\frac{28\,(\text{shadow of steeple})}{4\,(\text{shadow of man})}$$

$4x = 6(28) = 168$

$x = 168 \div 4 = 42$ feet

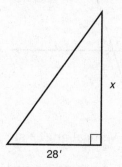

37. **1** $7 per book is 40% above cost or 140% of cost. 140% may be expressed as $1\frac{2}{5}$ or $\frac{7}{5}$.

Let x = cost.

$\frac{7x}{5} = 7$

$7x = 7(5) = 35$

$x = 35 \div 7 = 5$

The dealer's cost is $5 per book.

Six dozen books = $6 \times 12 = 72$ books

$5 \times 72 = 360, cost of books

38. **4** Since $B(5,4)$ and $D(5,-3)$ have the same x-coordinate (5), the line joining B and D is perpendicular to the x-axis and parallel to the y-axis. The distance from point B to the x-axis is 4, since the y-coordinate of B is 4. Since the y-coordinate of D is -3, the distance from the x-axis to D is 3. The total distance from B to D is $4 + 3 = 7$.

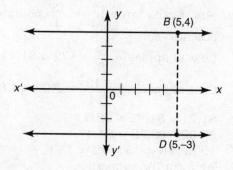

39. **3** $6 \times 10^5 = 600,000$

$4 \times 10^3 = 4,000$

$600,000 \div 4,000 = 600 \div 4 = 150$

40. **5** Slope $= \dfrac{y_1 - y_2}{x_1 - x_2}$

In this case, $y_1 = y$, $y_2 = 2$, $x_1 = 4$, and $x_2 = 1$.

Therefore, $\dfrac{y - 2}{4 - 1} = 1$

$\dfrac{y - 2}{3} = 1$

$y - 2 = 3$

$y = 3 + 2 = 5$

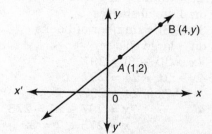

41. **4** The top of the bar for Wednesday is at 6 on the vertical scale.

42. **5** The top of the bar for Monday is halfway between 4 and 6, so 5 gallons were sold on Monday. The top of the bar for Saturday is halfway between 16 and 18, so 17 gallons were sold on Saturday. The difference between 17 and 5 is 12.

43. **4** The tops of the bars for Monday through Sunday are: 5, 4, 6, 5, 14, 17, and 9. These sum to 60.

44. **1** Let $x = $ m$\angle OAB$

$OA = OB$ since radii of the same circle have equal measures.

Therefore, m$\angle OAB = $ m$\angle OBA$:

$x + x + 70 = 180$

$2x + 70 = 180$

$2x = 180 - 70 = 110$

$x = 110 \div 2 = 55$

45. **3** Up to 4:00 P.M., Sylvia had traveled 124 miles. From the table we see that she was traveling at a steady rate of $124 - 80 = 44$ miles per hour. In $\frac{1}{4}$ hour Sylvia traveled $\frac{1}{4} \times 44 = 11$ miles. Thus, at 4:15 P.M. Sylvia had covered $124 + 11 = 135$ miles.

46. **2** If Joan uses a full cup of milk instead of $\frac{1}{3}$ of a cup she must multiply the measure of each ingredient by 3.

$3(\frac{2}{3}$ teaspoon of salt$) = 2$ teaspoons of salt

47. **4** This information can be read directly on the graph.

48. **4** Let x = cost of lot.
And $3x$ = cost of house.
$$x + 3x = 120,000$$
$$4x = 120,000$$
$$x = 120,000 \div 4 = 30,000$$
$$3x = 3(30,000) = \$90,000$$

49. **5** Let x = number of books on small shelf.
And $x + 8$ = number of books on large shelf.
$4x$ = number of books on 4 small shelves
$3(x + 8)$ = number of books on 3 large shelves
$$4x + 3(x + 8) = 297$$
$$4x + 3x + 24 = 297$$
$$7x + 24 = 297$$
$$7x = 297 - 24 = 273$$
$$x = 273 \div 7 = 39$$

50. **2** Diameter of outer circle =
$$40 + 4 + 4 = 48''$$
Radius of outer circle = $\frac{1}{2}(48) = 24''$

Diameter of inner circle = 40″
Radius of inner circle = 20″
We use the formula $A = \pi r^2$
Area of outer circle =
$\pi \times 24 \times 24 = 576\pi$
Area of inner circle =
$\pi \times 20 \times 20 = 400\pi$
Area of border = $576\pi - 400\pi = 176\pi$

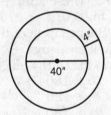

51. **1** 40 feet = $40 \times 12 = 480$ inches
3 feet 4 inches = $3(12) + 4 =$
$36 + 4 = 40$ inches
$480 \div 40 = 12$ scarfs

52. **2** If we write all the weights in ounces, it is easier to arrange the weights in order from the heaviest to the lightest. Recall that 1 pound = 16 ounces.

1 pound = 16 ounces, $\frac{1}{2}$ pound = 8 ounces

The correct order from the heaviest to the lightest is 20 ounces, 18.5 ounces, 16 ounces, 8 ounces, 7.95 ounces. The correct choice is (2).

53. **5** We check each pair of angles for congruence.

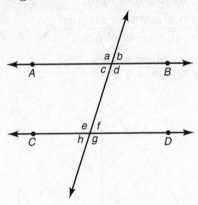

$\angle a \cong \angle d$. Vertical angles are congruent.
$\angle b \cong \angle f$. Corresponding angles of parallel lines are congruent.
$\angle c \cong \angle b$. Vertical angles are congruent.
$\angle f \cong \angle c$. Alternate interior angles of parallel lines are congruent.
There is no basis for saying that $\angle b$ is congruent to $\angle g$.
The correct choice is (5).

54. **1** $A + B + C = 180$
Since $A = B$, we may write
$B + B + C = 180$
Since $B = 2C$, we may write
$$2C + 2C + C = 180$$
$$5C = 180$$
$$C = 180 \div 5 = 36$$

55. **2** 6 ounces = $\frac{6}{16}$ of a pound = $\frac{3}{8}$ of a pound
Mrs. Evans buys $2\frac{3}{8}$ or $\frac{19}{8}$ pounds of apples
4 ounces = $\frac{4}{16} = \frac{1}{4}$ of a pound
Mrs. Evans buys $3\frac{1}{4} = \frac{13}{4}$ pounds of peaches
Cost of apples = $\frac{19}{8} \times .72 = \$1.71$
Cost of peaches = $\frac{13}{4} \times .56 = \$1.82$
$\$1.71 + \$1.82 = \$3.53$
$\$5.00 - \$3.53 = \$1.47$

56. **5** 15 dozen = $15 \times 12 = 180$
We form the proportion
$$\frac{6}{180} = \frac{39}{x}$$
$$6x = 39(180) = 7,020$$
$$x = 7,020 \div 6 = \$1,170$$

Answer Sheet for Practice Test Four

TEST 5: MATHEMATICS

1. ① ② ③ ④ ⑤
2. ① ② ③ ④ ⑤
3. ① ② ③ ④ ⑤
4. ① ② ③ ④ ⑤
5. ① ② ③ ④ ⑤
6. ① ② ③ ④ ⑤
7. ① ② ③ ④ ⑤
8. ① ② ③ ④ ⑤
9. ① ② ③ ④ ⑤
10. ① ② ③ ④ ⑤
11. ① ② ③ ④ ⑤
12. ① ② ③ ④ ⑤
13. ① ② ③ ④ ⑤
14. ① ② ③ ④ ⑤
15. ① ② ③ ④ ⑤
16. ① ② ③ ④ ⑤
17. ① ② ③ ④ ⑤
18. ① ② ③ ④ ⑤
19. ① ② ③ ④ ⑤

20. ① ② ③ ④ ⑤
21. ① ② ③ ④ ⑤
22. ① ② ③ ④ ⑤
23. ① ② ③ ④ ⑤
24. ① ② ③ ④ ⑤
25. ① ② ③ ④ ⑤
26. ① ② ③ ④ ⑤
27. ① ② ③ ④ ⑤
28. ① ② ③ ④ ⑤
29. ① ② ③ ④ ⑤
30. ① ② ③ ④ ⑤
31. ① ② ③ ④ ⑤
32. ① ② ③ ④ ⑤
33. ① ② ③ ④ ⑤
34. ① ② ③ ④ ⑤
35. ① ② ③ ④ ⑤
36. ① ② ③ ④ ⑤
37. ① ② ③ ④ ⑤
38. ① ② ③ ④ ⑤

39. ① ② ③ ④ ⑤
40. ① ② ③ ④ ⑤
41. ① ② ③ ④ ⑤
42. ① ② ③ ④ ⑤
43. ① ② ③ ④ ⑤
44. ① ② ③ ④ ⑤
45. ① ② ③ ④ ⑤
46. ① ② ③ ④ ⑤
47. ① ② ③ ④ ⑤
48. ① ② ③ ④ ⑤
49. ① ② ③ ④ ⑤
50. ① ② ③ ④ ⑤
51. ① ② ③ ④ ⑤
52. ① ② ③ ④ ⑤
53. ① ② ③ ④ ⑤
54. ① ② ③ ④ ⑤
55. ① ② ③ ④ ⑤
56. ① ② ③ ④ ⑤

TEST 5: MATHEMATICS

Tests of General Educational Development
Directions*

The Mathematics Test consists of multiple-choice questions intended to measure general mathematics skills and problem-solving ability. The questions are based on short readings that often include a graph, chart, or figure.

You will have 90 minutes to complete the questions in this test. Work carefully, but do not spend too much time on any one question. Be sure you answer every question. You will not be penalized for incorrect answers.

Formulas you may need are given on page 178. Only some of the questions will require you to use a formula. Not all the formulas given will be needed.

Some questions contain more information than you will need to solve the problem; other questions do not give enough information. If the question does not give enough information to solve the problem, the correct answer choice is "Not enough information is given."

The use of calculators is not allowed.

Do not write in the test booklet. The test administrator will give you blank paper for your calculations. Record your answers on the separate answer sheet provided. Be sure all information is properly recorded on the answer sheet.

To record your answers, fill in the numbered circle on the answer sheet that corresponds to the answer you select for each question in the test booklet.

FOR EXAMPLE:

If a grocery bill totaling $15.75 is paid with a $20.00 bill, how much change should be returned?

(1) $5.26
(2) $4.75
(3) $4.25
(4) $3.75
(5) $3.25

(On Answer Sheet)
① ② ● ④ ⑤

The correct answer is "$4.25"; therefore, answer space 3 would be marked on the answer sheet.

Do not rest the point of your pencil on the answer sheet while you are considering your answer. Make no stray or unnecessary marks. If you change an answer, erase your first mark completely. Mark only <u>one</u> answer space for each question; multiple answers will be scored as incorrect. Do not fold or crease your answer sheet. All test materials must be returned to the test administrator.

DO NOT BEGIN TAKING THE TEST UNTIL TOLD TO DO SO

* Reprinted with permission of the American Council on Education.

TEST 5: MATHEMATICS

FORMULAS*

Description	Formula
AREA (*A*) of a:	
square	$A = s^2$; where s = side
rectangle	$A = \ell w$; where ℓ = length, w = width
parallelogram	$A = bh$; where b = base, h = height
triangle	$A = \frac{1}{2} bh$; where b = base, h = height
circle	$A = \pi r^2$; where r = radius and π is approximately equal to 3.14
PERIMETER (*P*) of a:	
square	$P = 4s$; where s = side
rectangle	$P = 2\ell + 2w$; where ℓ = length, w = width
triangle	$P = a + b + c$; where a, b, and c are the sides
circumference (*C*) of a circle	$C = \pi d$; where d = diameter and π is approximately equal to 3.14
VOLUME (*V*) of a:	
cube	$V = s^3$; where s = side
rectangular container	$V = \ell wh$; where ℓ = length, w = width, h = height
cylinder	$V = \pi r^2 h$; where r = radius, h = height, and π is approximately equal to 3.14
Pythagorean relationship	$c^2 = a^2 + b^2$; where c = hypotenuse, a and b are legs of a right triangle
distance (*d*) between two points in a plane	$d = \sqrt{(x_2 - x_1)^2 + (y_2 - y_1)^2}$; where (x_1, y_1) and (x_2, y_2) are two points in a plane
slope (*m*) of a line	$m = \dfrac{y_2 - y_1}{x_2 - x_1}$; where (x_1, y_1) and (x_2, y_2) are two points on the line
mean	$mean = \dfrac{x_1 + x_2 + \cdots + x_n}{n}$; where the x's are the values for which a mean is desired, and n = number of values for x
median	The *median* is the middle value of an odd number of ordered scores, and halfway between the two middle values of an even number of ordered scores.
simple interest (*i*)	$i = prt$; where p = principal, r = rate, t = time
distance (*d*) as function of rate and time	$d = rt$; where r = rate, t = time
total cost (*c*)	$c = nr$; where n = number of units, r = cost per unit

* Reprinted with permission of the American Council on Education.

TEST 5: MATHEMATICS

Directions: Choose the <u>one best answer</u> to each question.

1. Luisa worked 40 hours and earned $6.30
   1. A salesman earns $200 per week plus a 5% commission on all sales over $8,000. One week, his sales amounted to $15,000. What were his earnings that week?

   (1) $200
   (2) $350
   (3) $500
   (4) $550
   (5) $600

2. How much does Jane pay for 1 pound 12 ounces of apples at $.84 per pound?

   (1) $1.36
   (2) $1.47
   (3) $1.57
   (4) $1.65
   (5) $1.75

3. One morning Martin drove 80 miles in 2 hours. After lunch, he covered 100 miles more in 3 hours. What was his average rate of speed, in miles per hour, for the entire trip?

   (1) 35
   (2) 36
   (3) 37
   (4) 45
   (5) Not enough information is given.

4. A picture 8 inches long and 6 inches wide is to be enlarged so that its length will be 12 inches. What is the width of the enlarged picture in inches?

   (1) 9
   (2) 10
   (3) 12
   (4) 14
   (5) 16

5. A man bought *ABC* stock at $19\frac{5}{8}$ and sold it at $23\frac{1}{4}$. What was his profit on 80 shares before deductions for commission and taxes?

   (1) $29
   (2) $240
   (3) $255
   (4) $290
   (5) $358

6. A solution of the inequality $3x - 1 < 5$ is

   (1) 3
   (2) 2
   (3) 1
   (4) 5
   (5) $2\frac{1}{2}$

7. A theater has 850 seats, 60% of which are in the orchestra. How many seats are in the balcony?

   (1) 240
   (2) 260
   (3) 320
   (4) 340
   (5) 510

8. In a right triangle, the ratio of the measures of the two acute angles is 4 : 1. What is the measure of the larger acute angle in degrees?

   (1) 50°
   (2) 54°
   (3) 70°
   (4) 72°
   (5) Not enough information is given.

GO ON TO THE NEXT PAGE

TEST 5: MATHEMATICS

9. If 18 feet 10 inches is cut from a wire that is 25 feet 8 inches long, what is the length of the wire that is left?

   (1) 6 feet 1 inch
   (2) 6 feet 2 inches
   (3) 6 feet 9 inches
   (4) 6 feet 10 inches
   (5) 7 feet 2 inches

10. Bill earns m dollars per month and Frank earns n dollars per month. How many dollars do both men earn in 1 year?

    (1) $12mn$
    (2) $12m + n$
    (3) $12(m + n)$
    (4) $12n + m$
    (5) $12n - m$

11. What is the perimeter of the figure below?

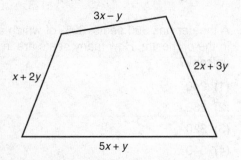

    (1) $11x + 5y$
    (2) $10x + 5y$
    (3) $11x + 4y$
    (4) $9x - y$
    (5) $8x + 3y$

12. Joan and Mary earn money by babysitting. If Joan earns twice as much as Mary and the two girls earn a total of $42, how much does Mary earn?

    (1) $8
    (2) $10
    (3) $12
    (4) $14
    (5) Not enough information is given.

13. The income tax form below gives the following instructions.

    If your taxable income is

At least	But not more than	Your tax is
0	$3,499	2% of the amount
$3,500	$4,499	$70 plus 3% of any amount above $3,500
$4,500	$7,499	$100 plus 5% of any amount above $4,500
$7,500		$250 plus 7% of any amount above $7,500

    How much tax is due on a taxable income of $5,800?

    (1) $120
    (2) $135
    (3) $150
    (4) $165
    (5) $175

GO ON TO THE NEXT PAGE

TEST 5: MATHEMATICS

14. Given the formula $x = 2a(b + 7)$, find x if $a = 3$ and $b = 5$.

    (1) 13

    (2) 72

    (3) 108

    (4) 120

    (5) 210

15. The weights of the eleven men on the Panthers football team are 201, 197, 193, 212, 205, 207, 195, 214, 198, 203, and 184. What is the median weight of a player on this team?

    (1) 199

    (2) 200

    (3) 201

    (4) 203

    (5) 205

16. A committee consists of 7 women and 4 men. If one member of the committee is chosen to act as chairman, what is the probability that the choice is a woman?

    (1) $\dfrac{1}{11}$

    (2) $\dfrac{1}{7}$

    (3) $\dfrac{4}{7}$

    (4) $\dfrac{7}{11}$

    (5) $\dfrac{10}{11}$

17. A bag of potatoes weighing 5 pounds 12 ounces costs $2.07. What is the cost of 1 pound of potatoes?

    (1) $.36

    (2) $.38

    (3) $.40

    (4) $.45

    (5) $.48

18. In the figure below, if $\overleftrightarrow{AC}$ is perpendicular to $\overleftrightarrow{CB}$ and m$\angle CBD = 125°$ then m$\angle A$ equals

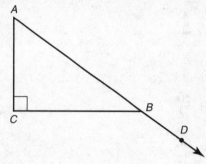

    (1) 15°

    (2) 20°

    (3) 35°

    (4) 45°

    (5) Not enough information is given.

19. In a large class 80 students took a test. When the test papers were rated, it was found that 10% of the students had A papers, 25% of the students had B papers, 30% of the students had C papers, 15% of the students had D papers and the rest failed. How many students failed the test?

    (1) 10

    (2) 12

    (3) 15

    (4) 16

    (5) Not enough information is given.

20. A man invests $20,000 to obtain annual interest at 7% and $12,000 to obtain annual interest at $7\frac{1}{2}$%. What was his annual income on the two investments?

    (1) $1,400

    (2) $1,500

    (3) $2,000

    (4) $2,300

    (5) $2,800

GO ON TO THE NEXT PAGE

TEST 5: MATHEMATICS

21. A dozen eggs cost x cents. What is the cost of 3 eggs at the same rate in cents?

    (1) $\dfrac{x}{3}$

    (2) $\dfrac{x}{4}$

    (3) $\dfrac{3x}{4}$

    (4) $\dfrac{x}{12}$

    (5) $3x$

22. Pete Rossini has just graduated from college with honors. He has been offered desirable jobs with the following pay provisions:

    A. $27,000 for the first year
    B. $570 per week for the first year
    C. $2,250 per month for the first year
    D. $2,000 per month for the first 6 months and an increase of 10% for the last 6 months

    Which of the above offers will give Pete Rossini the greatest income for the first year?

    (1) A
    (2) B
    (3) C
    (4) D
    (5) Not enough information is given.

23. A dealer bought two dozen jackets at $48 each. The next month he bought 15 more jackets at $48 each. Which of the following expressions gives the number of dollars the dealer spent for the jacket?

    (1) $24 \times 48 + 15$
    (2) $(24 \times 48) \times 15$
    (3) $24 + 48 \times 15$
    (4) $48(24 + 15)$
    (5) $24 + (48 + 15)$

24. One car travels at an average speed of 48 miles per hour. A slower car travels at an average speed of 36 miles per hour. How many more miles does the faster car travel than the slower car in 45 minutes?

    (1) 9
    (2) 10
    (3) 12
    (4) 27
    (5) 36

25. According to the graph below, by how many dollars do the sales in the meat department exceed the sales in the dairy department?

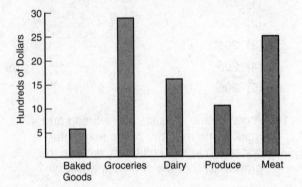

    (1) $100
    (2) $1,000
    (3) $1,500
    (4) $1,800
    (5) $10,000

26. A boat travels due east for a distance of 15 miles. It then travels due north for a distance of 20 miles, at which point it drops anchor. How many miles is the boat from its starting point?

    (1) 23
    (2) 25
    (3) 29
    (4) 30
    (5) 35

GO ON TO THE NEXT PAGE

TEST 5: MATHEMATICS

27. A man looked at the gauge of his 280-gallon oil tank on the first day of the month and found it to be $\frac{7}{8}$ full. At the end of the month, he observed that it was $\frac{1}{4}$ full. How many gallons of oil were used during that month?

    (1) 70

    (2) 105

    (3) 175

    (4) 210

    (5) Not enough information is given.

28. Express 2,750,389 in scientific notation.

    (1) 27.50389×10^5

    (2) 275.0389×10^3

    (3) 27.50389×10^6

    (4) $.2750389 \times 10^7$

    (5) 2.750389×10^6

29. A basketball team has won 50 games of 75 played. The team still has 45 games to play. How many of the games left to play must the team win in order to win 60% of all games played during the season?

    (1) 20

    (2) 21

    (3) 22

    (4) 25

    (5) 30

30. A rectangle and a triangle have equal areas. The length of the rectangle measures 12 inches and its width measures 8 inches. If the base of the triangle measures 32 inches, what is the measure of the altitude in inches?

    (1) 6

    (2) 8

    (3) 9

    (4) 12

    (5) 16

31. A school has 18 classes with 35 students in each class. In order to reduce class size to 30, how many new classes must be formed?

    (1) 2

    (2) 3

    (3) 5

    (4) 6

    (5) 8

32. According to the graph below, how many dollars were spent for labor?

Distribution of expenses for sales of $240,000 Ace Manufacturing Company

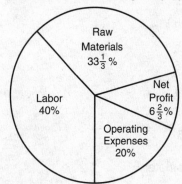

    (1) $4,800

    (2) $9,600

    (3) $48,000

    (4) $96,000

    (5) $960,000

GO ON TO THE NEXT PAGE

TEST 5: MATHEMATICS

33. What is the slope of the line joining point
    A (5,4) and point B (0,3) on the figure
    below?

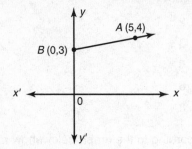

   (1) $\dfrac{1}{10}$

   (2) $\dfrac{1}{5}$

   (3) $\dfrac{3}{5}$

   (4) $\dfrac{4}{5}$

   (5) 5

34. 1 kilometer =

   (1) 10 meters

   (2) 100 grams

   (3) 1,000 liters

   (4) 1,000 meters

   (5) 1,000 millimeters

35. Given the equation $3x - y = 2$, which of the
    following pairs of points lie on the graph of
    the equation?

   A. (3,–2)
   B. (1,5)
   C. (2,4)
   D. (2,–2)
   E. (3,7)

   (1) A and B

   (2) C and E

   (3) B and C

   (4) A and E

   (5) B and D

36. If $3x - 1 = 11$, what is the value of $x^2 + x$?

   (1) 12

   (2) 15

   (3) 16

   (4) 18

   (5) 20

37. A bell rings every 2 hours, a second bell
    rings every 3 hours, and a third bell rings
    every 4 hours. If all three bells ring at
    9:00 A.M., when will all three bells ring
    again at the same time?

   (1) noon

   (2) 6:00 P.M.

   (3) 9:00 P.M.

   (4) 10 P.M.

   (5) Not enough information is given.

38. A family spends 20% of its monthly income
    on food, 23% on rent, 42% on other
    expenses and saves the balance. If the
    family saves $360 per month, what is its
    monthly income?

   (1) $2,000

   (2) $2,200

   (3) $2,400

   (4) $2,500

   (5) $28,800

GO ON TO THE NEXT PAGE

TEST 5: MATHEMATICS

39. In order to measure the distance across a pond (*DC*), shown in the figure below, a surveyor takes points *A* and *B* so that $\overleftrightarrow{AB}$ is parallel to $\overleftrightarrow{DC}$. If *AB* = 60 feet, *EB* = 48 feet, and *ED* = 80 feet, find *DC*.

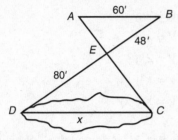

(1) 72 feet

(2) 84 feet

(3) 96 feet

(4) 100 feet

(5) Not enough information is given.

40. How many 4-inch by 8-inch bricks are needed to build a walk 6 feet wide and 24 feet long?

(1) 54

(2) 600

(3) 648

(4) 840

(5) 1,000

41. Each of the numbers below is a solution of the inequality $2x + 3 > 7$ EXCEPT

(1) 5

(2) 4

(3) 3

(4) 10

(5) 0

42. In the diagram below, what is the area of the triangle in square graph units?

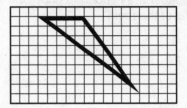

(1) 8

(2) 10

(3) 16

(4) 32

(5) 48

43. David Gordon is a bright high school senior planning to go to college. He has narrowed his choice to two colleges that he favors equally. He has decided to select the college that will be less costly. He used the following facts to help him arrive at a decision.

COLLEGE *A*
  Tuition — $9,480, Board and Lodging — $6,320. Books and incidentals — $1,200. David has been offered a scholarship of $4,200 per year.

COLLEGE *B*
  Tuition — $9,200, Board and Lodging — $6,150. Books and incidentals — $1,200. David has been offered a scholarship of $3,200 per year.
  David has also been offered a part-time job working in the college library.

What additional information does David need in order to make a choice?

(1) How many miles does he live from each college?

(2) Which college has the better reputation?

(3) How many scholarships does each college grant?

(4) How much can David earn by working in the college library at College *B*?

(5) Which college has better athletic facilities?

GO ON TO THE NEXT PAGE

TEST 5: MATHEMATICS

44. A room is 24 feet long, 18 feet wide, and 9 feet high. How many square yards of wallpaper are needed to paper the four walls of the room?

    (1) 72
    (2) 84
    (3) 96
    (4) 180
    (5) 756

45. A man drives x miles the first day, y miles the second day, and z miles the third day. The average mileage covered per day is

    (1) $\dfrac{xyz}{3}$
    (2) $\dfrac{xy+z}{3}$
    (3) $x+y+z$
    (4) $\dfrac{x+y+z}{3}$
    (5) $3xyz$

46. The diameter of a bicycle wheel is 28 inches. How many inches does the bicycle move when the wheel makes 10 complete revolutions? (Let $\pi = \dfrac{22}{7}$.)

    (1) 88
    (2) 440
    (3) 540
    (4) 750
    (5) 880

47. After working 4 hours Frank has made 21 machine parts. At the same rate, which expression below represents what he can accomplish in 7 hours? (Let x represent the number of machine parts Frank can make in 7 hours.)

    (1) $x = \dfrac{7(21)}{4}$
    (2) $x = \dfrac{7(4)}{21}$
    (3) $x = 7(21)$
    (4) $x = \dfrac{4(21)}{7}$
    (5) $x = 7(4)\,(21)$

48. A storage box in a form of a rectangular solid has a square base. If V represents the volume of the box, x represents the length of the base, and y represents the height of the box, which of the following equations expresses the relationship among V, x, and y?

    (1) $V = 2xy$
    (2) $V = xy^2$
    (3) $V = 2xy^2$
    (4) $V = x^2y$
    (5) $V = x + xy$

49. In his will, Mr. Adams left $\dfrac{1}{4}$ of his estate to his wife and divided the balance between his son and his daughter. If the son received \$36,000 as his share, what was the total value of the estate?

    (1) \$45,000
    (2) \$72,000
    (3) \$80,000
    (4) \$90,000
    (5) Not enough information is given.

Questions 50 through 52 are based on the following information.

A 3 foot wide walkway is built around a swimming pool that is 20 feet by 30 feet (see figure below). In order to determine how much flagstone to buy, the homeowner needs to know the total area of the walkway.

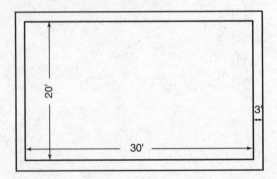

GO ON TO THE NEXT PAGE

TEST 5: MATHEMATICS

50. Which of the following expressions represents this area?

    (1) (20)(30)
    (2) (2)(3)(36) + (2)(3)(20)
    (3) (23)(33)
    (4) (2)(3)(30) + (2)(3)(20)
    (5) (26)(30)

51. If the average depth of the pool is 6 feet, what volume of water, in cubic feet, is needed to fill the pool?

    (1) 56
    (2) 300
    (3) 600
    (4) 3,000
    (5) 3,600

52. What is the total area (in square feet) needed for both the pool and the walkway?

    (1) 50
    (2) 62
    (3) 759
    (4) 936
    (5) Not enough information is given.

53. A map has a scale of 1 inch = 80 miles. Lakeville and Fulton are $3\frac{5}{8}$ inches apart on the map. What is the actual distance between Lakeville and Fulton, in miles?

    (1) 190
    (2) 290
    (3) 310
    (4) 325
    (5) 350

54. The regular price of a pair of slacks is *y* dollars. If the price is reduced by 20%, which of the following expressions indicates the cost of 3 pairs of slacks?

    (1) $\frac{4}{5}y$

    (2) $\frac{3}{5}y$

    (3) $3\left(\frac{4}{5}y\right)$

    (4) $3\left(\frac{3}{4}y\right)$

    (5) $3\left(\frac{1}{5}y\right)$

55. Mr. Downs is on a diet. For breakfast and lunch he consumes 40% of his allowable number of calories. If he still has 1,200 calories left for the day, what is his daily allowance in calories?

    (1) 800
    (2) 1,200
    (3) 1,500
    (4) 1,800
    (5) 2,000

56. A plumber must cut a pipe 64 inches long into two parts so that one part is 8 inches longer than the other part. Find the length of the larger part in inches.

    (1) 28
    (2) 30
    (3) 36
    (4) 40
    (5) Not enough information is given.

END OF EXAMINATION

Answer Key

1. 4	11. 1	21. 2	31. 2	41. 5	51. 5
2. 2	12. 4	22. 2	32. 4	42. 3	52. 4
3. 2	13. 4	23. 4	33. 2	43. 4	53. 2
4. 1	14. 2	24. 1	34. 4	44. 2	54. 3
5. 4	15. 3	25. 2	35. 2	45. 4	55. 5
6. 3	16. 4	26. 2	36. 5	46. 5	56. 3
7. 4	17. 1	27. 3	37. 3	47. 1	
8. 4	18. 3	28. 5	38. 3	48. 4	
9. 4	19. 4	29. 3	39. 4	49. 5	
10. 3	20. 4	30. 1	40. 3	50. 2	

Self-Analysis

WHAT'S YOUR SCORE?

_____right _____wrong

Excellent 51–56
Good 44–50
Fair 38–43

If your score was low, the explanation of the correct answers that follows will help you. You may obtain additional help by reviewing the self-analysis chart that follows.

Did you get at least 38 correct answers? If not, you need more practice for the Mathematics Test. You can improve your performance to Good or Excellent by analyzing your errors. To determine the areas in which you need further study, review the chart that follows. The question numbers from Practice Test Four appear in the column to the left. Circle the questions you answered incorrectly. (Unsolved problems are counted as incorrect.) Refer to the Chapter and Chapter Section indicated for each question for additional review.

SELF-ANALYSIS CHART

Question	Chapter	Chapter Section	Question	Chapter	Chapter Section
1	4	Percent	31	3	Types of problems
2	5	Weight measurement	32	7	Graphs
3	7	Analyzing data	33	6	Coordinates
4	4	Percent		4	Formulas
5	3	Types of problems	34	5	Metric measurement
6	4	Inequalities	35	6	Coordinates
7	4	Translation		4	Substitution
		Percent	36	4	Solving equations
8	6	Shapes			Substitution
9	5	Linear measurement	37	5	Measurement of time
10	4	Translation	38	4	Translation
11	6	Shapes			Solving equations
12	4	Translation	39	6	Shapes
		Solving equations	40	5	Linear measurement
13	7	Tables	41	4	Inequalities
14	4	Substitution	42	6	Shapes
15	7	Analyzing data		4	Formulas
16	7	Analyzing data	43	3	How to read a
17	5	Weight measurement			math problem
18	7	Lines and angles	44	6	Shapes
	6	Shapes	45	4	Translation
19.	3	Types of problems		7	Analyzing data
20	4	Formulas	46	6	Shapes
21	4	Translation	47	4	Translation
22	3	Types of problems	48	6	Shapes
	4	Percent		4	Translation
23	4	Translation	49	3	Types of problems
24	3	Types of problems		4	Translation
25	7	Graphs	50	6	Shapes
26	6	Pythagorean	51	6	Shapes
		relationship	52	6	Shapes
27	3	Types of problems	53	3	Types of problems
28	4	Scientific notation	54	4	Translation
29	4	Translation	55	4	Percent
		Percent	56	4	Translation
30	4	Types of problems			Solving equations

Answers Explained

1. **4** $15,000 − $8,000 = $7,000 sales over $8,000
   0.05 × $7,000 = $350 commission
   $200 + $350 = $550 total salary

2. **2** 12 ounces = $\frac{12}{16}$ pound = $\frac{3}{4}$ pound
   $1\frac{3}{4} = \frac{7}{4}$ pounds
   $\frac{7}{4} \times 0.84 = \$1.47$

3. **2** To obtain the average rate of speed, we divide the total distance covered by the total driving time.
   Total distance = 80 + 100 = 180 miles
   Total time = 2 + 3 = 5 hours
   180 ÷ 5 = 36 miles per hour, average rate of speed

4. **1** We use the following proportion
   $$\frac{\text{length of picture}}{\text{length of enlarged picture}} =$$
   $$\frac{\text{width of picture}}{\text{width of enlarged picture}}$$
   Let x = width of enlarged picture
   $\frac{8}{12} = \frac{6}{x}$
   $8x = 6(12) = 72$
   $x = 72 \div 8 = 9$ in.

5. **4** $23\frac{1}{4} = 22 + \frac{4}{4} + \frac{1}{4} = 22\frac{5}{4}$
   $22\frac{5}{4} = 22\frac{10}{8}$
   $\underline{\quad - 19\frac{5}{8}}$
   $\quad\quad 3\frac{5}{8}$
   $3\frac{5}{8} = \frac{29}{8}$
   $\frac{29}{8} \times \$80 = \$290$

6. **3** $3x - 1 < 5$
   $3x < 5 + 1$
   $3x < 6$
   $x < 2$
   Of the choices given the only choice less than 2 is 1.
   The correct choice is (3).

7. **4** 850 × 0.60 = 510 seats in orchestra
   850 − 510 = 340 seats in balcony

8. **4** Let $4x$ = the measure of the larger acute angle.
   And x = the measure of the smaller acute angle.
   $4x + x = 90$
   $5x = 90$
   $x = 90 \div 5 = 18$
   $4x = 4(18) = 72°$, measure of the larger acute angle.

9. **4** 25 feet 8 inches = 24 feet + 12 inches
   $\quad\quad\quad\quad\quad\quad\quad\quad$ + 8 inches
   $\quad\quad\quad\quad\quad\quad$ = 24 feet 20 inches
   $\quad$ 24 feet 20 inches
   $\underline{- 18 \text{ feet } 10 \text{ inches}}$
   $\quad$ 6 feet 10 inches

10. **3** Bill earns m dollars per month.
    Frank earns n dollars per month.
    Together Bill and Frank earn $(m + n)$ dollars per month.
    In one year, Bill and Frank earn $12(m + n)$ dollars.

11. **1** The perimeter of the figure is $(x + 2y)$ + $(3x − y)$ + $(2x + 3y)$ + $(5x + y)$.
    Perimeter = $(x + 3x + 2x + (5x)$ + $(2y − y + 3y + y)$
    Perimeter = $11x + 5y$

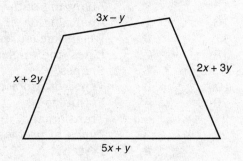

12. **4** Let x = Mary's earnings.
    And $2x$ = Joan's earnings.
    $x + 2x = 42$
    $3x = 42$
    $x = 42 \div 3 = \$14$, Mary's earnings

13. **4** $5,800 − $4,500 = $1,300
    Tax is $100 + 5% of $1,300 =
    100 + 0.05(1,300) = 100 + 65 = $165

14. **2** $x = 2a(b + 7)$
    $x = 2(3)(5 + 7)$
    $x = 2(3)(12)$
    $x = 72$

15. **3** To find the median weight we arrange the weights in order of size and identify the middle weight. In order of size the weights are
    184, 193, 195, 197, 198, 201, 203, 205, 207, 212, 214
    The middle (or sixth weight) is 201.

16. **4** Probability =
    $$\frac{\text{number of successful outcomes}}{\text{total number of outcomes}}$$

In this case, the number of successful outcomes is 7 and the total number of outcomes is 11.

Probability = $\dfrac{7}{11}$

17. **1** 12 ounces = $\dfrac{12}{16}$ = $\dfrac{3}{4}$ of a pound

5 pounds 12 ounces = $5\dfrac{3}{4}$ = $\dfrac{23}{4}$ pounds

If $\dfrac{23}{4}$ pounds cost \$2.07, then 1 pound costs $2.07 \div \dfrac{23}{4}$.

$2.07 \div \dfrac{23}{4} = 2.07 \times \dfrac{4}{23} = \$.36$

18. **3** $m\angle CBD = 125°$
$m\angle ABC = 180° - 125° = 55°$
$m\angle A + m\angle ABC = 90°$
$m\angle A + 55° = 90°$
$m\angle A = 90° - 55° = 35°$

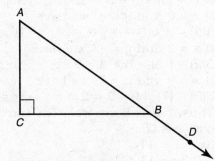

19. **4** 10% had *A* papers
25% had *B* papers
30% had *C* papers
15% had *D* papers
80% had passing papers
20% had failing papers

20% of 80 = $\dfrac{1}{5}(80) = 16$

20. **4** $\$20,000 \times 0.07 = \$1,400$

$7\dfrac{1}{2}\%$ written as a decimal = 0.075

$\$12,000 \times 0.075 = \$900$
$\$1,400 + \$900 = \$2,300$

21. **2** If a dozen eggs cost *x* cents, 1 egg costs $\dfrac{1}{12}x$ cents. 3 eggs cost $3\left(\dfrac{1}{12}x\right)$

which may be written as $\dfrac{3}{12}x$.

$\dfrac{3}{12}x$ reduces to $\dfrac{1}{4}x$, or $\dfrac{x}{4}$.

22. **2** We calculate the yearly income for each choice.
  A. \$27,000
  B. $\$570 \times 52 = \$29,000$
  C. $\$2,250 \times 12 = \$27,000$
  D. $6 \times \$2,000 = \$12,000$ for the first half-year
    10% of \$2,000 = \$200
    $\$2,000 + \$200 = \$2,200$ each month for the second six months
    $6 \times \$2,200 = \$13,200$ for the second half-year
    $\$12,000 + \$13,200 = \$25,200$ for the first year
The correct choice is (2).

23. **4** The distributive property states that
$a(b + c) = a \times b + a \times c.$
We may represent the number of dollars spent by the dealer as
$48(24 + 15)$
Note that $48(24 + 15) =$
$48 \times 24 + 48 \times 15.$

24. **1** 45 minutes = $\dfrac{45}{60}$, or $\dfrac{3}{4}$ of an hour
At 48 miles per hour, the faster car covers $\dfrac{3}{4} \times 48$, or 36 miles.
At 36 miles per hour, the slower car covers $\dfrac{3}{4} \times 36$, or 27 miles.

$36 - 27 = 9$ miles

25. **2** Meat department sales = \$2,500
Dairy department sales = \$1,500
Difference = \$1,000

26. **2** We use the Pythagorean theorem.
$x^2 = (15)^2 + (20)^2$
$x^2 = 225 + 400$
$x^2 = 625$
$x = \sqrt{625} = 25$ miles

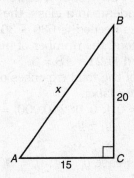

27. **3** $\dfrac{7}{8} - \dfrac{1}{4} = \dfrac{7}{8} - \dfrac{2}{8} = \dfrac{5}{8}$ of full tank of oil used

$\dfrac{5}{8} \times 280 = 175$ gallons used

28. **5** To express a number in scientific notation, we express it as the product of a number between 1 and 10 and a power of 10. In this case, the number between 1 and 10 is 2.750389. In going from 2.750389 to 2,750,389 we move the decimal point 6 places to the right. Each move represents a multiplication by 10 and 6 moves represents a multiplication by 10^6. Thus,

$$2{,}750{,}389 = 2.750389 \times 10^6$$

29. **3** The team has played 75 games and will play 45 more games.
$75 + 45 = 120$
60% of $120 = 0.6 \times 120 = 72$
The team must win 72 games and it has already won 50 games. Therefore, the team must win $72 - 50 = 22$ more games.

30. **1** The area of the rectangle = base × altitude = $12 \times 8 = 96$ sq in. The area of the triangle =
$\frac{1}{2}$ base × altitude = $\frac{1}{2}$ $(32)(x) = 16x$
$16x = 96$
$x = 6$ inches

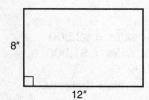 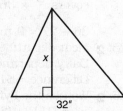

31. **2** The number of students in the school is $18 \times 35 = 630$. If there are to be 30 students in a class, the number of classes needed is $630 \div 30 = 21$. Therefore, the number of new classes needed is $21 - 18 = 3$.

32. **4** 40% of the total expenses of $240,000 went for labor.
$40\% = 0.4$; $0.4(\$240{,}000) = \$96{,}000$

33. **2** Slope = $\dfrac{y_1 - y_2}{x_1 - x_2}$
In this case $y_1 = 4$, $y_2 = 3$, $x_1 = 5$ and $x_2 = 0$.
Slope = $\dfrac{4 - 3}{5 - 0} = \dfrac{1}{5}$

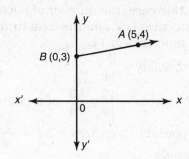

34. **4** 1 kilometer = 1,000 meters

35. **2** If a number pair satisfies an equation, then the point named by the number pair lies on the graph of the equation. We try the number pairs in turn.

$$3x - y = 2$$

If $x = 3$ and $y = -2$, we have
$3(3) - (-2) = 9 + 2 = 2.$ Not true
If $x = 1$ and $y = 5$, we have
$3(1) - (5) = 3 - 5 = 2.$ Not true
If $x = 2$ and $y = 4$, we have
$3(2) - 4 = 6 - 4 = 2.$ True
If $x = 2$ and $y = -3$, we have
$3(2) - (-3) = 6 + 3 = 2.$ Not true
If $x = 3$ and $y = 7$, we have
$3(3) - (7) = 9 - 2 = 2.$ True
Thus, C and E are true. The correct choice is (2).

36. **5** $3x - 1 = 11$
$3x = 11 + 1 = 12$
$x = 12 \div 3 = 4$
$x^2 + x = (4)^2 + 4 = 16 + 4 = 20$

37. **3** The first bell rings at 9:00 A.M., 11:00 A.M., 1:00 P.M., 3:00 P.M., 5:00 P.M., 7:00 P.M., 9:00 P.M., 11:00 P.M., 1:00 A.M., 3:00 A.M., 5:00 A.M., 7:00 A.M.
The second bell rings at 9:00 A.M., 12:00 noon, 3:00 P.M., 6:00 P.M., 9:00 P.M., 12:00 midnight, 3:00 A.M., 6:00 A.M.
The third bell rings at 9:00 A.M., 1:00 P.M., 5:00 P.M., 9:00 P.M., 1:00 A.M., 5:00 A.M.
All three bells ring again at 9:00 P.M.

38. **3** The family spends $20\% + 23\% + 42\% = 85\%$. The family saves $100\% - 85\% = 15\%$ of its monthly income.
Let $x = $ family monthly income.
15% of $x = 0.15x$
$0.15x = 360$
$x = \dfrac{360}{0.15}$ 15 $= \dfrac{36000}{15} = \$2{,}400$

39. **4** Let $x = DC$.
Since $\triangle ABE$ is similar to $\triangle CED$, the lengths of the corresponding sides of the two triangles are in proportion.
$$\frac{x}{60} = \frac{80}{48}$$
$48x = 80(60) = 4800$
$x = 4800 \div 48 = 100$ ft

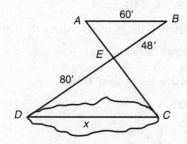

40. **3** The width of the walk is 6 feet, or $6 \times 12 = 72$ inches. The width of each brick is 4 inches.
The number of bricks that can be fitted along the width is $72 \div 4 = 18$.
The length of the walk is 24 feet, or $24 \times 12 = 288$ inches. The length of each brick is 8 inches. The number of bricks that can be fitted along the length is $288 \div 8 = 36$.
$18 \times 36 = 648$

41. **5** We check each of the numbers in turn.
$2(5) + 3 > 7, 10 + 3 > 7.$ True
$2(4) + 3 > 7, 8 + 3 > 7.$ True
$2(3) + 3 > 7, 6 + 3 > 7.$ True
$2(10) + 3 > 7, 20 + 3 > 7.$ True
$2(0) + 3 > 7, 0 + 3 > 7.$ Not true
The correct choice is (5).

42. **3** The area of the triangle is given by the formula $A = \frac{1}{2} bh$.
In this case, $b = 4$ and $h = 8$.
Area $= \frac{1}{2}(4)(8) = 16$

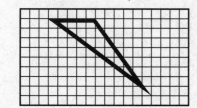

43. **4** In order to make a sound financial decision, David must know how much he can earn by working in the College B library.

44. **2** Area of front wall =
$9 \times 24 = 216$ sq ft
Area of back wall =
$9 \times 24 = 216$ sq ft
Area of side wall =
$9 \times 18 = 162$ sq ft
Area of other side wall =
$9 \times 18 = 162$ sq ft
Area of walls =
$216 + 216 + 162 + 162$
Area of walls = 756 sq ft
$756 \div 9 = 84$ sq yd

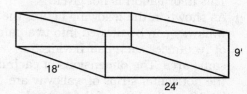

45. **4** To find the average we divide the total mileage covered by the time consumed.
Total distance covered $= x + y + z$
Total time covered = 3 days
Average $= \frac{x + y + z}{3}$

46. **5** To find the circumference of the wheel, we use the formula $C = \pi d$.
In this case, $\pi = \frac{22}{7}$ and $d = 28$.
$C = \frac{22}{7} \times 28 = 88$ inches
Every time the wheel makes a complete revolution, the bicycle moves the distance of the circumference, or 88 inches.
In 10 complete revolutions, the bicycle moves $10 \times 88 = 880$ inches.

47. **1** Let $x =$ the number of machine parts Frank can make in 7 hours.
We use the proportion
$$\frac{4}{21} = \frac{7}{x}$$
$4x = 7(21)$
$x = \frac{7(21)}{4}$

48. **4** We use the formula $V = lwh$.
In this case, $l = x$, $w = x$, and $h = y$
$V = x(x)y$
$V = x^2y$

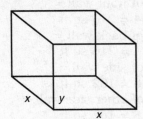

49. **5** We cannot find the value of the estate unless we know the daughter's share. This information is not given.

50. **2** As shown in the following figure, the walkway can be divided into two pairs of rectangles each pair having the same area. The dimensions of each of the horizontal strips of walkway are 3 by 36, while those of the vertical strips of walkway are 3 by 20. Since there are two rectangles of each size, the total area can be found as $(2)(3)(36) + (2)(3)(20)$.

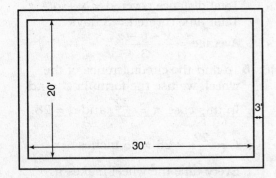

51. **5** Since the average depth of the pool is 6 feet, the water forms a rectangular solid with dimension 30 by 20 by 6. The volume of the water is the product of these three numbers $(30)(20)(6) = 3600$.

52. **4** Taken together, the pool and the walkway form a rectangle with dimensions 36 by 26, so the total area is the product $(36)(26) = 936$.

53. **2** Lakeville and Fulton are $3\frac{5}{8}$ inches apart on the map. Since 1 inch = 80 miles, 3 inches = $3(80) = 240$ miles.

Since 1 inch = 80 miles, $\frac{5}{8}$ inch = $\frac{5}{8}(80) = 50$ miles.

$240 + 50 = 290$ miles.

54. **3** $20\% = \frac{1}{5}$

$\frac{5}{5} - \frac{1}{5} = \frac{4}{5}$

The reduced price of a pair of slacks is $\frac{4}{5}y$

The reduced price of 3 pairs of slacks is $3\left(\frac{4}{5}y\right)$

55. **5** For breakfast and lunch Mr. Downs consumes 40% of his allowable number of calories. Thus, Mr. Downs has 60% of his allowable number of calories left for the day.
Let x = number of allowable calories per day.
$0.60x = 1,200$
$x = 1,200 \div 0.60$
$x = 1,200/0.60 \times 100/100 =$
$120,000/60 = 2,000$

56. **3** Let x = the length of the shorter part.
And $x + 8$ = the length of the longer part.
$x + x + 8 = 64$
$2x + 8 = 64$
$2x = 64 - 8 = 56$
$x = 56 \div 2 = 28$
longer part
$= x + 8 \quad = 28 + 8 = 36$

NOTES

NOTES

NOTES

NOTES

NOTES

NOTES

NOTES

NOTES